The Story of

KNIGHTS AND ARMOR

The Story of
KNIGHTS AND ARMOR

by ERNEST E. TUCKER

illustrated by

W. T. MARS

LOTHROP, LEE AND SHEPARD COMPANY, INC. • NEW YORK

Third printing, November, 1966

© 1961 by Ernest E. Tucker
Library of Congress Catalog Card Number: 61-15443

To my son, Ernest H. Tucker, *who
likes to hear stories about great
deeds and high adventure, this book
is affectionately dedicated.*

Table of Contents

FOREWORD: The Stone Knight on the Tomb 11

CHAPTER 1: Saracen Attack: A.D. 1191 17

CHAPTER 2: Arrows, Spears, and Chariots 33

CHAPTER 3: Forward, the Legion: 57 B.C. 41

CHAPTER 4: The Horseman Takes Over 53

CHAPTER 5: The Death of Huberic Split-Chin: A.D. 637 61

CHAPTER 6: The Man on Horseback Enters 75

CHAPTER 7: Caballarius of Charlemagne: A.D. 801 83

CHAPTER 8: The Sea Robbers 97

CHAPTER 9: The Knighting of Drogo the Red: A.D. 1066 105

CHAPTER 10: The Training of a Knight 123

CHAPTER 11: Nick, the Clumsy Squire: A.D. 1107 133

CHAPTER 12: Iron Clothes and Stone Houses 151

CHAPTER 13: Sir Roger's First Tournament: A.D. 1184 165

CHAPTER 14: Afternoon and Evening 185

CHAPTER 15: Harry the Gunner: A.D. 1359 197

AFTER-WORD 213

The Story of

KNIGHTS AND ARMOR

In a quiet village in the southeast of England there is a tumble-down little church. Parts of it are very old, older even than the carved stone figure of a knight in armor which lies in a dim corner of the church.

The stone effigy is that of a man in chain mail. Whoever carved it was a clever sculptor. The knight looks as if he had been lying asleep, with his head on his shield, and was awakened suddenly, perhaps by an alarm of attack. He seems about to spring to his feet. One hand is reaching for the great sword beside him. Over his chain mail is a surcoat, and on the surcoat the sculptor has put a cross, and so we know the figure is that of a Crusader. But the device on the shield is worn smooth. No one can tell what it once showed.

Men who study history have examined the stone figure and decided the unknown knight died somewhere between the years 1220 and 1260. That is all they know about him. They are able to tell that much because of the kind of armor he is wearing and the weapons he has. But his name, where he lived, or how he died—everything else is a mystery. Nobody knows anything more about him, not even old Jamie Wickford, who has been sexton of the little church for sixty years.

Jamie doesn't even know whether the knight is really buried under the stone. Not that it makes much difference, because after seven hundred years nothing would be left except a handful of dust and maybe a few links of broken iron. He shows the stone figure to visitors. He is proud of the stone knight, but he is prouder of the tombs of people he knew.

He always calls attention to the tomb of Captain the Honorable Frederick Benton-Thornhill, who won the Victoria Cross—England's highest military award—for bravery in World War I. Captain Benton-Thornhill was killed in 1915 in a little town in Belgium. Old Jamie is proud, too, of the marble slab bearing the names of four townsmen who died in World War II. One was Leading Seaman Frank Warren, killed on convoy duty on the murderous sea lanes to Russia. Another was Air Force Group Captain Finley Thornhill, who vanished in his bomber one night in 1944, somewhere over Germany.

In the little churchyard lie buried seven American fliers who crashed while they were returning from a mission in 1943. One of them was Staff Sergeant Ralph Wicker, of Olney, Illinois. Ralph's parents came to the little English town two years after the war ended, to see where their son was buried. Jamie told them there had been a family of Wickers in the town, but they had all died or moved away long ago. "Maybe you are related to our Wickers," he said to the people from Olney.

There are many others buried in the churchyard. Most of them vanished from everyone's memory long ago. Even the markers of their graves have gone. Some day Jamie expects to lie in the same churchyard, along with his father and mother, and his grandfather and the other Wickfords. There have always been Wickfords in the town.

When Jamie told the Wickers of Illinois that they might be related to the English Wickers, he was quite right, although he didn't know it. They were related, though very distantly, through a Wicker who had gone to the American colonies in the year 1713. The Wickers were related to Leading Seaman Frank Warren also, and to the Honorable Frederick Benton-Thornhill, and to old Jamie himself. Scattered around the world—in England, the United States, Canada, Australia, and many other places—are distant cousins of Staff Sergeant Ralph Wicker of Olney, Illinois.

12

The Wickers looked at the stone knight on the tomb, too, but the sculptured figure didn't mean much to them. Mr. Wicker didn't know that he, and all the others, were descended from the unknown Crusader.

★   ★   ★

The Crusader's name was Sir Roger de Wyke. He was born in the year 1164, in a fortified manor house which stood about two hundred yards from where the church is now. There was a church there in Sir Roger's day too, but all that is left of it is a few stones in the foundation of the present church. Nothing at all remains of the manor house.

Sir Roger was a knight in the days when a knight's business was fighting and nothing else. He spent most of his life fighting—against the Scots, far to the north; against the French; against rebels and outlaws. But most of all against the Saracens.

In 1190, he followed his king, Richard the Lion-Hearted, to the Holy Land to take back the Holy City of Jerusalem from the Mohammedan Saracens. Richard wasn't a very good king, but he was a wonderful fighting man, and Roger was one of the best knights in his army.

Let's take a closer look at Sir Roger to see how he and other knights fought and what they fought with.

Sir Roger is worth a closer look. Not because he was handsome, or courtly, or gracious, or kind, the way knights are supposed to have been. Roger wasn't at all handsome. He was awkward anywhere except on a field of battle. He was good to his family, and

they loved him, but no one would have called him a kind man. Roger could read—not very well—and write his own name, but he looked on that kind of thing as beneath him, and left it to clerks and monks, whose business it was. He believed in witches and ghosts and goblins, in dragons and giant birds that could carry a man away.

In short, he was not a bit like the romantic pictures of the Knight in Shining Armor. But he was rugged, brave, tough, strong, and honorable—a good knight, in the days when a knight was a fighting man and nothing else.

Sir Roger de Wyke opened his eyes, blinked, yawned, and sat up on the blanket that had served him for a bed. Outside his tent he heard men and horses moving. Voices passed the tent and someone laughed. It was hardly daylight yet, but already the air was hot.

He grunted and stood up. Roger was wearing only a pair of knee-length linen drawers, and even these were torn and frayed. He scratched his head, then various other places where fleas had breakfasted on his tough hide. The fleas had been his bedmates. He didn't mind fleas; never in his life had he slept in a flealess bed. He would have been uneasy without them.

Walking the few steps to the tent flap, Roger peered out. Most of his sixty men were already up, eating their scanty breakfast and getting ready to move out.

Saracens were in the neighborhood. There would be fighting today.

Not that Roger minded fighting. That was his business. He was good at it, and he enjoyed it. Still, it was a harebrained errand he had been sent on—trying to find a secluded valley where the natives were supposed to have hidden their sheep and goats from the invading Crusaders. Of course there was no such valley, and Roger's sixty men were a long way from King Richard's main army.

With luck, they would find the army tomorrow, or the day after. It was marching slowly southward toward the Holy City of Jerusalem, which was held by the infidel Saracens. Roger's job was to get his men back safely.

Well, they'd never get started if he stood here blinking out at the camp and the scrubby, yellow land beyond it. "Mahsoor!" Roger bawled. "Mahsoor!"

His little Syrian body servant came up on the run, smiling and bowing humbly. He carried an earthen flask of wine and a chunk of dark bread on which lay two small fish. The knight took them and tore off a huge mouthful of bread and fish in his strong jaws, chewing fishbones and all, and washing them down with a long drink of the sour Palestinian wine.

"Come on," he ordered Mahsoor, turning back into the tent.

"G-g-good day, Roger," said a voice, and a mournful face with a long drooping mustache poked itself into the tent. It was Sir Guy de Seyle, called The Stammerer, who always looked as if he were on the verge of tears but was really a savage and ruthless fighter.

Roger only grunted.

"G-g-going to be as hot as the p-p-pit today," Guy said cheerfully.

"Always is," Roger said, scowling at Mahsoor. He had a scar which ran from his eye down past his mouth, and the scowl made it doubly dreadful. Poor Mahsoor flinched at the sight.

There were other scars on Roger's body. Some were souvenirs of fighting in France or on the Scottish border. Some he had received in tournaments. A few were new, acquired since he had come to the Holy Land in the train of Richard. One scar, under his left arm, was still red and tender; a Saracen had made that with his keen scimitar, a second before he departed for the Moslem paradise under Roger's sword.

The scars were the signs of Roger's business. All knights and men-at-arms had them. Roger had been lucky. He still had all his teeth, unlike Ugo of Terrasina, who had been hit in the mouth by a rock. And Roger's ears were intact, except for a small piece from the tip of one.

18

His beard was untended, patchy where hairs had caught on the links of his mail hood and been pulled out. He kept meaning to shave but never got around to it. Mahsoor had given him a haircut, an uneven, saw-toothed kind of haircut, with a knife. Roger's hands and face were burned dark brown by the fierce sun, but the rest of his body was white. At least, comparatively white. Only three weeks ago he had had a bath.

He finished the bread and fish, took a last swallow of wine, and tossed the empty flask onto his bed. "Shirt," he said to Mahsoor. The little servant brought his long-sleeved linen shirt. As Roger raised his arms to put it on, great pads of muscle stood out on his neck and shoulders—muscle he needed to swing his heavy weapons. His tremendous barrel-chest did not taper to the slim waist the ladies admired so much. Sir Roger needed the weight and strength of a sheath of muscle over his belly. His legs seemed a little short for his weight. They were somewhat bowed, thick and knotted.

The shirt had been washed by Mahsoor, after a fashion. Then came long stockings which fastened to the shirt by strings. Mahsoor had forgotten to wash them, and the less said about their condition the better, but Roger was not a fastidious man.

Now he was ready for arming. The wine and bread had cheered him a little, and he grinned at Guy. "Go get them lined up," he said. "I'll be out in a minute."

Guy nodded, and looked at the gambeson which Mahsoor held out apologetically. Guy, too, was anything but finicky, but he wrinkled his nose at the gambeson. It was a thick, padded, knee-length garment which protected the wearer from the chafing of his mail. Roger's was a good one, lovingly made by his mother and sisters, but it was stiff with old sweat and blood, caked with dirt, altogether a noisome thing.

"S-s-stinks, doesn't it?" remarked Guy helpfully.

"You'd be more use getting the men ready to march than standing around complaining about my gambeson," Roger growled. Guy laughed and went out.

After the gambeson came another pair of stockings, thicker ones, and soft leather shoes. Roger was not even in his armor yet, and already sweat was beginning to roll down his face and neck. With

Mahsoor's awkward help, he struggled into his chain mail leggings. It took a good deal of tugging and swearing to get these adjusted and fastened by straps to a belt.

Then came the hauberk, the most expensive and necessary part of his armor. It was a shirt of linked iron rings, each one forged separately and riveted together. The hauberk was shaped like the gambeson under it, slit in front and back so the wearer could mount a horse. It weighed nearly fifty pounds, and poor little Mahsoor could hardly lift it over Roger's shoulders.

It seemed to take forever to get the clumsy thing over his head, work his arms into the sleeves, and lace it up under his chin. The hauberk had been mended many times, where a scimitar or mace had broken some of the links, but Roger had been too busy to have an armorer overhaul it. Mahsoor had tried to mend the broken places with leather thongs, and had rubbed it every night with sand, but there were still patches of rust on what should have been brightly shining links.

When it was finally in place, Roger squatted a few times, swung his arms, then nodded. It felt right.

He was nearly finished. From outside the tent came shouts and the sound of hoofs, as his men formed up. "Hurry," Roger said. Sweat was pouring from him now. On his head he put a steel cap, padded on the inside. Over that came the mail hood, or coif, drawn tight with a thong.

He hadn't taken along his big, heavy, pot helmet on this expedition. Many a knight had suffocated in that helmet, in the terrific heat of the Holy Land.

Roger shook his head when Mahsoor offered his gauntlets, heavy leather mitts with iron rings sewed to their backs. He hated the things and accepted the added risk of having a hand lopped off. Next, the servant got down on his knees to fasten to his master's heels the gilt spurs, symbol of knighthood. The gilt was worn off,

21

but Roger, although he had been a knight for seven years, was still very proud of them.

He put on his Crusader's surcoat, a long, loose, sleeveless garment. Once white, it was now yellowish, and the red cross had faded to a brick color. Last of all came the wide leather belt which supported his sword on the left side and his dagger on the right. He drew the heavy, straight sword for a few practice swings, and Mahsoor cowered.

Over his shoulder Roger hung his shield. Not the shield he had brought from England; that had been shattered in his first battle. A Syrian artisan had made this one—kite-shaped, of tough wood covered with leather, bound in brass and studded with brass nail-heads. On a red field it bore the wide diagonal white stripe and the golden lamp which was the badge of the de Wykes.

Now he was armed, ready for whatever the day might bring. Bending stiffly, he went out of the tent, blinking in the morning glare. His little army was standing ready, and there was a small stir when they saw him. A crowd of ragged natives from the miserable village nearby watched fearfully. They hoped that the Franks —they called all Europeans Franks—would go on their way and leave them to their poverty.

There were six knights in the band of sixty that Roger led. The rest were mounted men-at-arms, or esquires, apprentice knights. In addition, there were a few servants, like Mahsoor, and grooms for the horses. Some of the men-at-arms were from Roger's own meinie, or feudal following, and all were English except a few Burgundian men-at-arms and Sir Gerhard von Seewald, a big Bavarian with a fist like a ham, slow-witted but a mighty fighter. All the men wore some sort of armor, even if it was only a leather corselet. They all looked, and were, tough.

The Stammerer came forward. "All r-r-ready," he reported.

Roger nodded. "Old sour face," he said affectionately. "You shouldn't look at a man before he has breakfast, Guy. That camel's face of yours turns his stomach."

Guy was not in the least offended. "If you want to s-s-stand and talk all d-d-day," he said reasonably, "we'll n-n-never get s-s-started."

Mahsoor came up, leading the horse Roger would ride. It was an old, half-blind gelding which he had bought at a ruinous price from a Venetian trader. In England, he wouldn't have been caught dead on such a wreck, but horses died easily in the Holy Land and many a poor knight had none. A knight might better lack a sword than a horse. Roger wanted to spare his own war horse as much as he could, and so he mounted his destrier, or fighting horse, only if a battle was imminent. Meanwhile the destrier, Puppet, was under the care of a young Englishman of feeble wits named Tom, the only one except Roger who was able to handle the savage brute.

Roger climbed aboard the aged beast, whose head drooped even lower at the prospect of carrying three hundred pounds of armored knight across the desert. He gave an order to Guy, his second-in-command. Guy raised his arm and the little army rode off.

In a few minutes the squalid collection of mud huts which made up the Palestinian village was lost to view, as the path wound among hills covered with scrub and thorn brush. Guy sent those with the best horses to act as outriders—ahead, along the flanks, and behind—to guard against the sudden attack which was a Saracen specialty.

He was riding beside Roger, when the sun popped up from behind the hills to the east. A sound like a sigh came from the men. They knew what the Holy Land sun was like.

"I've b-b-been wondering," Guy said in a conversational tone, "how that b-b-brute of a horse of yours ever got a name like Puppet."

Roger grinned. "My little sister Constance named him when he was newborn. He had been promised to me, and I wanted some name like Hero or Champion. But when Constance gets her mind fixed on something—" He shook his head. "She's the only one who can do anything with him. And Tom, of course. I can manage him when I'm on top of him, but I don't think Puppet likes me very much."

"He d-d-doesn't like anybody," Guy said, and they lapsed into silence until he exclaimed suddenly, "Saracens about. I can s-s-smell 'em."

"I know." Roger could smell them too—a fighting man developed the power of sensing when an enemy was nearby. "We'll have to fight our way back to the army. The closer Richard gets to Jerusalem, the more Saracens come out of the hills to stop him. I'm surprised they haven't found us before now."

"They will," Guy said cheerfully. "They will."

It was getting too hot to talk. Even after all these months since Richard had landed at Acre, Roger still could not get used to the terrible heat of the Holy Land. It made him feel like a wrung-out sponge. He was no longer sweating. His body felt dry. Now and then he moistened his lips with warm water from his leather water bottle, but he knew better than to take more than a sip at a time.

The water had a foul taste. Every time he took a sip, Roger thought of the little brook near his father's manor house. How cool it was! And how he had loved to go wading in it when he was a boy, and to try to catch the little fish which darted back and forth in the silvery water!

He shook his head. No good thinking about that. Some day, God willing, he would see the brook again. Meanwhile he had other things to worry about. He touched the mail of his sleeve with his bare hand, and it burned.

Guy said mournfully, "I f-f-feel as if I were carrying a pot of live c-c-coals on my head."

24

The little army was winding along the bed of a dry watercourse. The horses' hoofs stirred up powdery yellow dust that covered everything, and soon men and beasts alike were the same ugly yellow as the landscape. The men hawked and spat as dust got into their mouths and nostrils.

The sun was nearly overhead when a faint shout came from in front of them. Roger held up his hand and the column halted. One of the scouts returned, waving his lance.

The enemy! There was a stir and noise behind Roger as he turned his head and called, "Form up!" He swung awkwardly to the ground as Simple Tom hurried up with Puppet. Roger climbed to the destrier's back, and Tom mounted the old horse, giving his master the lance he had been carrying—a twelve-foot pole of ashwood with a diamond-shaped iron head.

Roger had forgotten all about the brook at home. "Thirty men in the first line," he said crisply. "Twenty in the second—under you, Gerhard. Ten in reserve. You take them, Blaise. You know what to do."

The other knights nodded and swung back to take their places. "Guy, beside me. If I fall, take command."

"You won't fall," Guy said. With battle imminent, he had lost his stammer. The melancholy look had gone from his face, and his eyes shone. He shook his lance.

The scout, a wide-eyed esquire of seventeen, rode up with a speed that set his long fair hair flying. "Sir Roger! Saracens ahead! Riding straight for us!"

"All right, Dick," Roger said. "Quiet down. We're ready for them. How many?"

"About two hundred," the boy said, and Roger nodded. Over the stamp of hoofs and the rattle and clank of weapons, he could hear faraway shouting and the thump of kettledrums. Saracens loved those drums.

The lines of battle formed. Sixty men didn't make much of an army, but they went about their business in a way that showed they knew what to do. The second line stayed about fifty yards behind the first. A hundred yards to the rear were the reserves. They would move in when and where they were needed. Sir Blaise would know. A stout fighter and a crafty one.

The drumming and shouting got louder. Roger's outriders appeared and took their places in the lines. Someone shouted, "There they are!"

Over the crest of the hill ahead poured a mob of shrieking Saracens. They were a dazzling sight—graceful horses, flowing robes, the fluttering green and black banners of Islam, sun glinting

on waving scimitars. Roger didn't appreciate the beauty of the sight. He merely muttered a curse against the infidel and gripped his lance tighter.

He knew these raids. The Saracens would not meet the fearful charge of the mailed Franks head-on—they knew that if they did, they would be ridden into the ground. Instead, they would circle and shoot arrows, darting in quickly to swing their keen scimitars, trying to confuse the slower-moving Franks.

"Forward!" Roger shouted. The first line moved ahead, holding their lances aslant.

The wave of Saracen horsemen was less than two hundred yards away. Now they should begin to turn and circle. But these raiders

kept coming, riding straight at the Crusaders. They were going to smash right into the line! Roger grinned. They must be from some far-off part of Sultan Saladin's wide dominions. They hadn't met the Franks yet. They'd learn.

The Crusaders were yelling now. Their ponderous war horses broke into a trot, then a gallop. Puppet's great hoofs pounded the earth and his powerful muscles moved smoothly under Roger's thighs. The destrier whinnied in excitement. He knew that the fluttering, noisy creatures ahead of them were enemies.

Roger couched his lance, and the other lances came down, thirty iron points aimed straight at the onrushing enemy. His narrowed eyes peered over the top of his shield as he sighted at a Saracen in a green cloak. Roger was thoroughly enjoying himself.

On each side the line thundered forward. At the last minute the Saracens wavered. One tried to rein his horse around. Too late.

With a tremendous shock and crash the lines met. Clouds of dust almost blinded Roger. His lance slammed into the Saracen in the green cloak, tore through shield and armor and spitted him like a lamb.

"De Wyke!" he roared. "De Wyke!" The Saracen's body flopped for a second on his lance shaft, and he shook it off savagely.

Shouts, screams, trampling of hoofs, smell of blood, neighing of angry horses, clash of weapons, pounding of kettledrums. A Saracen aimed a blow with his scimitar. Roger swept his lance sideways and knocked the man from his horse. Before him rose a dark, bearded face, the mouth wide open in a yell, the eyes glazed with fury. The Saracen thrust with his spear. Roger caught the spear on his shield, and his lance slammed into the open mouth.

Beside him, Guy was singing at the top of his lungs. Guy always sang when he fought, and always the same song:

"My love's eyes are tender, my love's eyes are true..."

28

He never sang that song except when he was killing someone.

The pressure eased for a moment, and Roger rose in his stirrups to look around. The Saracens, with their greater numbers, had surrounded the little army of Crusaders. Sir Blaise had swept his reserve into the battle to keep from being separated.

But the terrible charge of the Crusaders had ridden right through and over the Saracens, smashing them under the horses' hoofs, trampling them into the ground. Now the enemy had drawn back a little. Their leaders were waving their scimitars and screaming for another attack, but seemed to be getting small response. The Saracens were brave men and good fighters, but they were too light to stand up under such an onslaught. Obviously they had not expected any such demons in human form as these mailed Franks.

"We'll hit 'em again," Roger bawled at Guy, who nodded. The line surged forward again toward the milling Saracens.

But suddenly the kettledrums began beating a different rhythm —the signal to withdraw. The army of Saracens wavered, then turned and fled.

"Hold!" Roger bellowed, as some of his men began to ride after them. "Stand fast!" It would be death to let the men get strung out, following the infidels back to their hills.

"Form a line," he ordered. His lance dripped blood. His surcoat was half torn from his body. On the ground lay nearly sixty Saracens, slain in the few minutes of battle. They looked like little heaps of cloth thrown carelessly down on the desert. Roger wasted no thought on them. On the ground, too, were eight dead Crusaders, including Sir Blaise, who had commanded the reserve. A gallant knight. Fourteen others were wounded, and their comrades were already binding their hurts, helping them onto horses, or mounting them behind uninjured men. No orders needed to be given. Every man knew what to do—they had all done it before.

"What of our dead, Roger?" Guy asked. "Should we try to take them back for decent burial?"

Roger shook his head. "Here they must stay. We have to press on. They died on holy ground, fighting for the Cross, and they're looking down on us from Heaven this minute."

"Aye, you're right," Guy said. "God rest their souls for brave men."

"Amen." Roger ran his eyes down the line of his followers. "Where's Simple Tom?"

"Dead, sir," young Dick reported. "So is your other horse."

Roger had grown up with Simple Tom. Although the fellow didn't have all his wits, he could call birds from trees and rabbits from their burrows. Tom had never quite understood what the fighting was about. Ah, well, he had died a soldier—and what more could a man ask?

Puppet was excited and hard to handle. His nostrils quivered at the smell of blood. Roger called, "Forward," and the line moved ahead slowly. Again scouts moved out to guard against surprise. In the hills to the north Roger saw the flicker of a green cloak.

"Well, it was a g-g-good fight while it lasted." Guy's stammer was back, now that the excitement was over.

"They'll come again," Roger said. "And they'll bring every bee in the Saracen hive. From now on we'll be watched."

"True," Guy agreed cheerfully. "But next t-t-time they'll know better than to run head-on into our lances. I got three at the f-f-first shock—lined them up one after the other on my lance like p-p-pieces of meat on a spit."

"Oh, you're a wonder, you are," said Roger.

He was not worried over their situation. But, he admitted to himself, he wasn't exactly overjoyed at it either. Fifty-two fighting men and a few servants, some of them wounded, surrounded by foes— and a long road ahead. Well, he would do what he could. And after all, it was in the hands of God. They had come here to fight for God and He would protect them. If they were killed, they were assured of Heaven. It was as simple as that. So why worry?

Guy was right. It had been a good fight while it lasted.

The sun was lower in the sky but the heat was worse, if anything. The layers of padding and metal on Roger's body held the heat and made him think of the way the foresters cooked fowl at home—covered with clay and set on the coals to bake.

There would not be another attack until tomorrow, probably. It would take the Saracens that long to get over their shock. Maybe, Roger thought, we can make it to the sea first. And maybe not. But I won't let it bother me.

As they rode along, Roger found himself humming The Stammerer's fighting song:

"My love's eyes are tender, my love's eyes are true..."

Roger and Guy, riding across the dusty, hot hills toward the army of King Richard, had no real doubt that they would get there. They were full of confidence in their own ability as fighting men, and of contempt for any Saracens they might meet.

As commander of the expedition, Roger had a good deal on his mind. He had to see that the column did not straggle, watch the horizon for signs of the enemy, and keep check on his outriders.

But Sir Guy, The Stammerer, fell into a reverie as he rode along. He was more of a scholar than Roger, and he was impressed by the fact that for thousands of years, fighting men had been marching up and down this same stretch of country. Egyptians, Assyrians, Israelites—a thousand forgotten armies in a thousand forgotten wars. Maybe Julius Caesar himself had led an army of Romans along this route, Guy thought. Or Alexander the Great, or the splendid kings of long-gone times like David or Nebuchadnezzar. He looked around at the low hills, imagining an endless army of Greeks, Romans, and Israelites, marching along.

When he thought of them, however, he pictured mounted knights similar to himself and Roger. He thought of Alexander and Julius Caesar as wearing chain mail hauberks and coifs, riding destriers, and armed with long lances and heavy, straight swords.

It never occurred to Guy that there had been a time when there were no mounted knights—heavy cavalry. Born and raised in an age when heavy cavalry was the deciding force in battle, he despised

33

soldiers who had to fight on foot. Nobody had ever told him that the mounted man had taken over the leading role in war only a few centuries before. Until then, cavalry had been only auxiliary troops —useful enough, but not to be relied on. Guy would have been shocked and angry if anyone had tried to tell him that.

He would have been even more shocked to be told that already, in those dying days of the twelfth century, the mounted knight and all he stood for were on the way out, and in a few hundred years he would be only a museum piece.

Heavy cavalry—which is all knights were, really—took over suddenly, and dramatically, in a battle in the late fourth century A.D. between Roman legionaries and barbarian horsemen. Before that, the Roman foot soldier had been the mainstay of the army, and before him, the heavy infantry of Alexander. Greeks and Romans both had cavalry, but the horseman was a comparatively minor figure, useful for scouting and quick raids. To win battles, the generals relied on the man on foot.

Of course men had been riding horses for thousands of years. As soon as a primitive herdsman managed to climb aboard a wild horse without having his leg chewed off, he began thinking about how he could use his new skill to annoy his neighbors. It didn't take him long to figure out how, and cavalry was born.

In ancient times, the only cavalry that amounted to anything belonged to Oriental kings. The wide plains of Asia were perfect for horsemen and chariots. They still are, and in Asiatic countries armies have regiments of cavalry even today. Men armed with short rifles and swords look up from their saddles to watch jet bombers roar overhead. Shouting tribesmen still gallop over the steppes where the armies of Assyria and Persia moved.

The ancient Orientals went in for light cavalry, mostly mounted bowmen. Those empires of half-forgotten times used chariots also, two-wheeled carts drawn by one or two, or even four, horses. The charioteer was generally too busy to do any real fighting himself, but one or two combat men rode with him. There might be an archer or a javelin-thrower, and a spearman or swordsman who would jump off the chariot and do his fighting on foot—a primitive equivalent of today's airborne troops. Chariot wheels were sometimes fitted with sharp blades to cut down enemy soldiers the way a lawnmower cuts grass.

Most countries abandoned chariots in fairly early times. They looked impressive, rolling along with a great rumble, throwing up clouds of dust, but they were clumsy things, hard to maneuver and

always breaking down. They were worthless in rough or broken country. Besides, the enemy soon caught on to the way of dealing with chariots: cripple a horse, break a chariot wheel, dig a trench, or just get behind breastworks—and the chariot couldn't hurt you.

The ancient light cavalry was fine for covering a lot of ground

in a hurry. But you couldn't capture walled cities with cavalry. Nor was it very successful against trained infantrymen. A war between two countries which depended on light cavalry was likely to consist mostly of riding around and shouting, of quick raids, cattle stealing, and small encounters, without very much being accomplished. Even the ancient Orientals depended heavily on foot soldiers.

When the Greeks started nudging their way onto the center of the stage, they knew nothing about cavalry. But they learned about it from the warriors of the East, and being Greeks, took over the idea and beat the Orientals at their own game.

The Greeks worked out combinations of cavalry and infantry which for a long time were unbeatable. But still the heavily armed infantryman, the "hoplite," was the core of the army, and battles were won or lost according to how well he fought. He fought pretty well, on the whole, and the Greeks beat the best the Orientals could send. Then along came Alexander, king of Macedon, whom men called "The Great."

Alexander conquered most of the known world with his "pha-lanx," a plan of battle formation he inherited from his father, Philip. The phalanx was a square made up of about 5,000 men armed with pikes, great spears eighteen to twenty-two feet in length. In battle, a phalanx looked like a giant porcupine. The pikes were so long that a soldier could stand four or five ranks back and still be able to poke a sharp point into an enemy. There wasn't much you could do with a phalanx except get out of its way. No matter which way you approached it, you were met by a mass of bristling spear-points.

But the phalanx had one great drawback. It needed steady, disciplined men who would hold their formation against any attack and work together as a unit. Under Philip and Alexander, the men in the phalanx waded stolidly ahead, always pointing their pikes straight at the enemy's face. Alexander could discipline them. But

Alexander died at the age of thirty-three, after a wild party, and the men who followed him were not up to the job. Instead of a disciplined square, the phalanx became a crowd of farmhands tripping over one another's pikes.

Greece declined into a hodgepodge of little quarreling states, and new leaders took over.

These were the Romans, who brought the art of fighting on foot to its highest peak until the days of Frederick the Great, seventeen hundred years later. At their best, the Roman legions were unbeatable. They lacked the fire and originality of the Greeks, but they had everything else: courage, discipline, self-confidence, and a kind of stubbornness all their own. At first Rome was a republic, with an army of citizen soldiers, tough and patriotic. They were beaten, but they didn't stay beaten, and they were never fooled more than once by the same trick.

The Romans rarely conceived anything new, but they had the knack of turning other people's ideas to their own use. They fought a series of wars with the people of Carthage, in North Africa, their greatest rivals. The Romans couldn't get at Carthage itself because, hating the sea, they had no navy. But the Carthaginians were a seafaring people. So the Romans captured a Carthaginian ship and built a navy by constructing replicas. They were amateurs at shipbuilding and their first navy sank. This didn't discourage them; they turned right around and built a better one. That was the way they did things. In the end, they conquered Carthage—not only conquered it, but destroyed it so completely that what had been the wealthiest city in the world was turned into a desert.

Once the Roman legions started to march, they kept right on marching. They marched over Alexander's old territory. They marched into the wealthy Orient. They marched into Africa, over Gaul, over Spain, over a foggy island off the west coast of Europe. Rome owned everything worth owning.

The Romans were very handy little men. Wherever they went, they built roads and bridges so that they could get back in a hurry if they had to, or could bring up more soldiers. They never camped for the night without constructing a fort complete with embankments of earth and a palisade of sharpened stakes. A cautious people, the Romans. The fort went up even if there were no more chance of their being attacked than there would have been on their own Via Flaminia, in the middle of Rome itself.

The Roman army was organized much like modern ones, with ranks equivalent to corporal, sergeant, captain, and general. They also had a fine corps of engineers, who built the wonderful roads and bridges. They had artillery: catapults and rams. They had cavalry, skirmishing troops, and a quartermaster department to feed them.

But the backbone of the army was the legionary, the heavily armed foot soldier. He was a muscular, square-jawed man, short by modern standards—five feet three inches was a good average height. He marched all day at an unvarying pace, carrying a load that would overwhelm a modern infantryman. Besides his weapons and armor, each legionary carried a long sharpened stake for a palisade, a sack of flour, several flat pieces of hardtack, cooking tools, a jug of water or wine, spare clothes, and other odds and ends.

He wore a bronze or leather helmet, a corselet—body armor—of strips of bronze or toughened leather, and carried a semi-cylindrical shield. This equipment varied from province to province and from century to century, but remained basically the same. Once a legionary of Julius Caesar's army learned the current slang, he would have been right at home in the army of the emperor Septimius Severus, more than two hundred years later. If things changed that slowly now, we would still be wearing powdered wigs and velvet breeches.

One of Sir Roger de Wyke's ancestors was a legionary in the army of Julius Caesar. His name was Quintus Rufinus Strabo. He marched with the Numidia Legion in the days before Caesar crossed the Rubicon, became dictator, and was assassinated. Q. Rufinus Strabo became a general before he died. But long before that he was just a red-faced country boy pretending to be an old soldier.

On the day he fought his first battle, he was scared to death.

Quintus Rufinus Strabo, a legionary in the First Century of the First Cohort of the Numidia Legion, swung along a cart track in Northern Gaul, near the Rhine River. He was excited. Also—though he dared not admit it to his companions or even to himself—he was scared.

Numidia Legion was on its way to fight a battle. People were killed in battles. Other people were wounded, like old Tassio, a handyman on the farm belonging to Quintus' father. Tassio wasn't good for much, with his one arm, except to sit in the sun and tell stories of how he had got his wound. Quintus did not have an over-active imagination, but he couldn't get rid of the thought of himself sitting in the sun with one arm.

Not that this was a big battle he was heading for. The commanding general in Gaul, Caius Julius Caesar, had not even come along on the expedition. It was only a matter of punishing some German tribesmen who had slipped across the Rhine and stolen some cattle. They had also burned a Gaulish town and, what was worse, ambushed and slain a Roman patrol. This sort of thing could not be allowed to go unpunished; other Germans might be inspired with the idea that they could do the same thing. So Numidia Legion, under a general who had come up from the ranks, Publius Terentius Carus, had marched off to wipe out a few Germans and restore quiet.

Quintus was a recruit. That is, he had served eighteen months, but had not yet fought a battle. He was a good soldier and he liked camp life, the rough comrades, the exercises with sword and javelin.

He even liked his one-eyed centurion, Flavius Cocles, although he would rather have been flogged than admit it to his friends.

Quintus was square and strong, and handled weapons well. If he lived he could hope to become a centurion, commander of a hundred. Maybe "primus pilus," first centurion of the 6,000-man legion. Maybe even, although this was unlikely, a general like old P. Terentius Carus.

Quintus had caught the eye of his officers during his first weeks in the army, when a bullying four-year veteran tried a brutal kind of hazing on him. Quintus threw the bully into the cooking pot. When the bully brought back two of his friends and tried again, Quintus grabbed a broken javelin shaft and sent them off howling. The young recruit was punished, but the officers had noticed his strength and pugnacity—and that was why he found himself in the First Century of the First Cohort, lugging his shield among veterans of many battles.

He griped and joked with the best of them as they marched along, but he couldn't quiet the nervous flutter in his stomach. His comrades, as old soldiers will, filled his ears every night with stories of carnage and mutilation. Now, on their way to fight the Germans, all Quintus heard was how tough they were, how big and brawny— one swipe of a German battle-ax could split a man in two—and how horribly they treated prisoners.

Fascius Larens, a ten-year man who had taken Quintus under his wing, was recalling battles with the Germans. All his stories ended the same way—Roman recruits being hacked into gobbets of flesh by howling German warriors. Quintus knew that Fascius was trying to scare him, but he couldn't help feeling there was *some* truth in what the old-timers were saying. So he grinned and kept quiet, as a recruit should, while the six thousand men of the legion, plus eight hundred slingers and skirmishing troops, tramped along the empty banks of the river Rhine.

They camped early that night, first putting up their stakes in a square, ditching and embanking, digging latrines, erecting platforms for sentries—all the routine Quintus grumbled about every night, but which he knew perfectly well had to be followed. All night long there was a coming and going of messengers and runners from the general's tent. The legion was formed up early. It was still dark, and they were not allowed fires for breakfast. Wild rumors flew: there were a hundred thousand Germans ahead of them; the Gauls had revolted and joined the Germans; bad omens had been seen; the Numidia was marching to sure destruction.

Fascius grunted at Quintus in a surly tone as they fell in: "Take a good look at the sun, boy. Last time you'll see it."

One rumor was confirmed by the centurions: an army of Germans was close ahead of them on the west bank of the Rhine, howling defiance and offering fight.

The light infantry ran out ahead as a scouting and screening force; the legion marched after them. There was a tongue of forest in front of them that worried the general—he didn't want to be ambushed there. But the scouts reported that the Germans were still milling around on a rolling plain beyond, shouting and arguing about who was going to lead the attack against the hated Romans. Safely through the forest, the legion deployed on the plain. The Germans were less than a mile away; Quintus could see smoke from their cooking fires. No cold breakfast for them!

Slingers took their positions as the legion formed up. So far, it was all just like parade ground. Horns blared, cymbals clashed, centurions cursed, soldiers grumbled. They might as well have been on the Campus Martius in Rome as on some nameless plain near the end of the world.

The general was up ahead on his horse, surveying the situation. Quintus saw him nod, satisfied. He himself could not see the Germans because a low hill was in the way.

In battle formation Quintus stood about four feet from Fascius, on his left, and a chunky soldier known as The Curly Hog on his right. The second rank of the shock troops stood diagonally behind the front rank, the third rank directly behind the front rank, and so on, checkerboard-fashion, with about eight feet separating the ranks. Around each century of a hundred men was a space for maneuvering. This open formation gave each man plenty of room to use his weapons, since he was not jammed tightly in a close-packed huddle. Each man, and each century could move forward or sideways at need. Men could slip back through the ranks, if wounded or ordered to retreat. In the rear of the legion were ranked the older men, armed with long pikes instead of the short throwing spears. If it became necessary, they could form a defensive phalanx.

Quintus swung his shield forward on his shoulder. In his left hand he gripped his "pilum," the combination lance and throwing spear which was a favorite Roman weapon. In his right hand he held a lighter javelin. Around him there was a clatter as each man did the same thing.

The familiar routine and noises were restoring Quintus' courage. He had supreme confidence in his weapons, in his comrades, and—he was beginning to discover—in himself. Confidence was needed in such an open formation, which worked successfully only with tough, disciplined men. When confidence lagged, the centurion had told them a thousand times, discipline slipped; and when that happened a legion became only a crowd of men huddling together, seeking comfort in company—and an army became a mob.

Quintus' confidence was not misplaced. The Roman sword and pilum were among the great weapons of all time. The pilum, eight feet long with a razor-sharp head and a long iron shank, served equally well as a missile or a shock weapon. A husky legionary could throw it accurately with a terrific impact. Quintus was an expert with the pilum; long hours of hurling it at wooden targets had developed his natural talent. But he liked the sword best. When he was a boy cutting grain with a sickle, he had pretended he was a soldier lopping off his enemies' heads. He had been a little disappointed to discover that the army preferred jabbing with a sword to swinging it, until he learned why.

The Romans had found out early that a man will stand bravely to a swinging sword, leaning into the blow and catching it on his shield, but there is something about a steel point reaching for his belly that turns his blood to water. Also, to attack with the short "gladius," the soldier had to get in close, and that meant he pressed forward constantly, never giving his enemy a chance to get set, shoving him back on his heels. And as the Roman pressed forward, the enemy fell back. Or died. Or killed the Roman—but then there was always another Roman who stepped in and took his place, always another gladius stabbing out. Barbarians couldn't stand much of that.

For this little battle, old General Carus was not bothering with any elaborate tactics. His orders were a straight line of battle—strike ahead and push the Germans back across the river; kill enough of them so it would be a long time before they ventured into Roman territory again; take some prisoners.

The legionaries stood easily, resting on their spears. The Curly Hog, who was never without something to eat, took some raisins from a pouch and popped them into his mouth. Fascius yawned and closed his eyes. Quintus pretended to be unconcerned, too, but his heart was hammering.

From the Germans, still unseen over the hill, came a long-drawn roaring which seemed to be getting closer. The light infantry must have met them by now. Once Quintus heard the howl of a man in agony, and little prickles of sweat began to run down his back under his coarse tunic.

When he got a little older, he learned that for all their outward calm even the veterans were taut and excited. But now he was still

45

a raw recruit, and he envied them their impassive faces and tried to imitate them. The centurions paced endlessly up and down the lines, squinting into the face of each man to see if any showed signs of possible breaking. One-eyed Flavius came past, and Quintus managed to grin at him, getting back a wink from the centurion's single eye. The Curly Hog ate some more raisins and fished a chunk of goat cheese from his pouch.

By stretching his neck a little, Quintus could see the first rank of legionaries, extending from a thick wood on his left to the river on his right. The farm boy felt a swell of pride as he saw the long line of men, each holding his shield and javelin ready. He felt a strength and sureness which came from knowing himself to be a part of this awesome display, knowing it to be only a small part of the strength of Mother Rome, feeling the invisible bonds which stretched back over plain and mountain, binding him to the crooked streets and white temples of the old city on the Tiber.

Now there was movement ahead. From over the hill, trotting toward the legion, came some of the light infantry, breathing hard but looking unperturbed and not at all tired. They were Spaniards, tough men and good fighters, but not legionaries—not really Romans at all. They were armed with light javelins, swords, and wicker shields, and wore armor of overlapping leather scales. Their job was simply to reconnoiter, harass the enemy, slow him down. One of them grinned at Quintus and said in thick Latin: "We have weakened them for you, little man. Now it's safe to move!"

The Spaniards and slingers filtered back through the ranks, exchanging taunts with the legionaries.

Quintus was startled by the sudden blast of a war horn. Other horns took up the braying. Moving ahead of the line was the gold standard of the Numidia. "Forward!" Flavius Cocles bawled, and as one man the legionaries stepped out. Quintus grasped the straps of his shield, balanced his javelin, and trotted forward.

"Keep line!" shouted the decurion, commander of ten. "Keep up, Curly Hog, may Jove blast you! Marcellus! Quit crowding! You don't have to lean on his shoulder!"

There was a steady thud, thud of feet. Weapons clanged. War horns and drums kept up their racket. Through it all the decurions cursed and yelled at their men.

The first rank surmounted the hill.

Below it were the Germans. Their roaring sounded louder, now that the hill was no longer between them and the legion. They bounded forward in little groups, without formation, waving axes and long swords. Scattered skirmishing was still going on between the Germans and the light infantry, but the barbarians had seen the legionaries and were anxious to get at them.

There were thousands of Germans. In front ran the chiefs, calling on their followers. Quintus heard one big fellow howling like a wolf. He had a wolf's skin over his shoulders and wore the animal's head as a kind of cap. Some of the Germans were blowing horns. Many were bounding up and down in eagerness or rage—Quintus couldn't tell which.

The Germans reached the base of the hill and began to mount. Centurions gestured and the legionaries went forward faster, their javelins raised to throwing position. The Romans were going downhill, the Germans up. General Carus had timed it well; the point of collision would come when the fury of the German charge had been slowed by their climb, when their line would be at its raggedest.

Quintus' nervousness had gone, but he didn't stop to think of that. He was straining to hear the signal to cast his javelin. Already he had picked the man in the wolfskin cap for his target—the man with a long yellow mustache who was still howling, waving a battle-ax and a round shield painted red and white.

Most of the legionaries were yelling too, drowning out the shouts of the decurions. Quintus was conscious of a fierce excitement and a yearning to get at the barbarians. A Roman javelin hurtled through the air, falling far short of the advancing Germans. No one had ordered the javelins cast, and with one corner of his mind Quintus thought: "There's one poor legionary going to get a taste of the grapevine whip!"

But now the centurion raised his arm and flung it forward.

Quintus braced himself, brought his arm back over his shoulder, and with a mighty heave hurled his javelin. With the same movement he transferred his pilum to his right arm.

Like a flight of birds the javelins split the air. They sliced into the front rank of the Germans. Few failed to find some mark in that close-packed mob.

There was a second of silence, then a mighty chorus of screams and yells. Men struggled on the ground. The Germans hesitated, then came on grimly, leaping over their fallen comrades. The man in the wolfskin was still on his feet. Quintus' spear had missed him but had plunged into the leg of another man, who was bowled over in the rush.

The Germans were almost upon the legion now. No time to cast by volley. The air was thick with thrown pilums. The Germans hurled their own weapons, lighter than the Romans' but still deadly. Quintus heard a hoarse gasp beside him, and from the corner of his eye saw The Curly Hog stumble and fall, a German javelin piercing his neck. His place was instantly filled by the legionary behind him.

Quintus threw his pilum and drew his sword.

The pilum hit the shield of the man in the wolfskin cap, went through it, and dragged the shield down on the German's arm, making it useless. Wolfskin shook his arm impatiently, trying to free it from the shield-strap.

Raising his own shield until he could just see over the top, Quintus held his sword ready for the thrust and went in. The German's immense ax was swinging up. Automatically, Quintus raised his shield to catch it. He felt the shock of the blow up to his shoulder, but the ax did no damage.

The German had stopped howling, and Quintus could hear his hoarse breathing. There was a spot just above his wide leather belt where a design was tattooed on his bare belly.

Quintus jerked the sword forward. The German screamed and folded up.

"Drive into 'em!" the decurion shouted. "Keep going! Marcellus, keep that shield up! D'you think this is a dance of the Vestal Virgins?"

A German was hacking at the shield of the man on Quintus' right. Quintus stumbled over the body of Wolfskin, caught himself, and chopped at the German's arm. The Curly Hog's replacement stabbed the German with his pilum.

Something clanged against Quintus' helmet. The point of something shiny appeared mysteriously sticking through his shield and as mysteriously disappeared. He saw a bare foot and stamped on it with his heavy boot. A hand grabbed his shield and tugged. He thrust, and the hand vanished.

Quintus was fighting by the instinct implanted in him by long months of practice. Don't bunch up. Go for the belly. Don't hold your shield in front of your eyes so you can't see. Keep your line straight. Protect the man on your right, and the man on your left will protect you. If you're wounded don't run, fall back—but Jove help you if you fall back unwounded!

He was conscious of a terrible press of swaying, sweaty bodies, of the thud and clang of steel and leather, the smell of blood, of grunts and yells and screams, and a sudden sharp pain in his right arm, which he immediately forgot.

Then all at once the pressure lessened. The German in front of him lifted his sword, seemed to think better of it, turned, and ran.

Quintus felt as if he were coming out of a dream. To his surprise, they were nearly at the riverbank. The slow, steady drive of the advancing legion had carried them four hundred yards from where the first clash began. Horns were sounding: Stop the advance! Forward through the ranks ran the Spaniards again, and the reserves, fresh men who would hunt down the fleeing enemy.

The decurion was still shouting: "All right, all right, stop and form up! You deaf, Marcellus? Want a bath in the river? Form up!"

He turned slowly. The battle was over. Auxiliaries, and some women who had come from Jove knew where, were already running across the battlefield, stripping the German dead. Scattered over the grassy plain lay hundreds of bodies, most of them German, but many Roman. The wounded Romans were being carefully tended, carried off on litters while the clash of battle still sounded in the woods behind them. The German wounded would be cared for, too—if it seemed likely they would recover. They made good slaves.

Quintus found Fascius limping and leaning on a German battle-ax.

"What hit you?" Quintus asked.

Fascius spat. "Nothing to worry about. Stuck in the leg. What hit you?"

For the first time, Quintus remembered that he had been wounded in the arm. "I don't know," he said, surprised. Now that he remembered his wound, he realized that it was hurting.

Flavius Cocles came by, dangling a necklace of amber with a gold pendant. "You all right, youngster?" he asked. Quintus nodded. "You'll make a soldier yet, young Quintus. Now get into line."

Quintus and Fascius found their century and formed up. There were more than a few empty places. Quintus felt tired and let down.

"We'll get bandaged up," Fascius said. "Then dig ditches. And put up the palisade. And dig latrines. And we'll both probably catch guard duty tonight." Then he brightened. "Maybe One-Eye will let me off, with this leg." He began limping dramatically.

It had not occurred to Quintus that the old routine would go on unchanged, after their great victory. "Anyhow," he said, "we beat them."

Fascius laughed scornfully. "Those amateurs? Those savages? Listen, boy, this wasn't even a good workout. Let me tell you about some *real* fights!"

He did, at great length, as they marched back slowly to the place where they would camp. Quintus listened, but some of his awe was gone. After all, he was a veteran now. He had fought in a battle himself, like the older men. Now he could tell recruits all about the terrible Germans—tell the young men who would be joining the Numidia to fill the places of The Curly Hog and the others.

★   ★   ★

Quintus fought the Germans again. And the Belgae, and the Helvetii, and the Britons, and many more.

Forty years from the day he and Fascius limped off an unnamed battlefield beside the Rhine, two old soldiers—General Quintus Rufinus Strabo, and a retired legionary named Fascius who kept a wineshop in Rome—talked about old times over a leather bottle of Fascius' best wine.

Fascius often boasted to his customers about how he and the general had served side by side, long ago, under the great Julius. "Taught the general his trade, I did," Fascius liked to say.

★   ★   ★

And a little more than eighteen hundred years later, a French soldier guarding a camp along the Rhine found a shapeless eroded piece of metal, turned up by a shovel. He skimmed it into the river, whistling *"Malbrouk s'en va-t-en guerre,"* and thought no more about it.

How could he know that the rusty flake had once been a sword—all that was left on this earth of The Curly Hog, soldier of the First Century of the Numidia Legion?

General Quintus Rufinus Strabo died wealthy and respected. He left a son who also became a general. But the son did not do as much fighting because there was not so much fighting to do. And the general's grandson was not interested in the army.

Why should he be? Life was more fun in Rome than sitting in some dreary fort on the Rhine. He went into politics and forgot pilum and gladius. He was a good politician, and managed to stay on top as emperors came and went. The Strabo family grew richer and more powerful. They held vast estates in Italy and Gaul and owned thousands of slaves. They kept busy making money and spending it, and having a wonderful time.

They, and a few other families, ruled Rome, and Rome ruled the world. They could afford anything they wanted, and they had it. Some of the young Strabos belonged to the army, but they did little except parade around in gilt armor.

For several generations the descendants of old Quintus Rufinus kept his wax death-mask among their family treasures, but they didn't pay much attention to it. When the mask was destroyed by fire in the reign of the Emperor Trajan, nobody cared. Quintus Rufinus was just a musty old name by then.

The Roman army still fought. The Strabos turned out like everyone else to cheer when the legionaries came marching back from a war on the empire's frontiers. The Romans never noticed that among the hard-muscled men in the legions were fewer and fewer real Romans and more and more Gauls or Britons or Germans. Nor did

they notice that most of the generals, too, were barbarians—big blond fellows hired to do the Romans' fighting for them.

They didn't even notice there were fewer and fewer Romans in the capital itself. Most of the old families were gone. More and more of the wealth was piling up in the hands of foreigners—Egyptians, Syrians and Greeks.

The Romans didn't notice and they didn't care. They were having too good a time. The army didn't matter much anyhow; there was no one left for the army to fight. During the centuries known as the Roman Peace—the Pax Romana—a legionary might spend a lifetime in service and never hurl his pilum against anything more deadly than a wooden post. Legions spent year after year doing nothing but leaning on their shields, looking over the Rhine, or the Orontes, or the Wall of Hadrian in northern England.

Most of the legionaries had never seen Rome. The Eternal City was just a name to them. They felt none of the patriotic sentiment that had inspired Quintus Rufinus, and the one-eyed centurion

Flavius Cocles, and even The Curly Hog. Instead of loyalty to Rome, the legionaries felt loyalty only to their legion, the only "country" they knew.

The legions lost the keen edge of discipline and the calm confidence that had inspired Quintus' men. They grew soft. No longer did they bother to build a fortified camp every night on the march; they just slept wherever they happened to be. It was too much trouble to carry stakes for a palisade, and besides, who in the world was going to attack them? Legionaries even complained that the pilum was too heavy, and so it was made lighter. It was still a good throwing weapon, but not worth much in close combat. They thought the armor was too heavy, and so that was made lighter as well.

Generals were afraid of new ideas. Four hundred years after Quintus Rufinus died they were still using much the same battle plans as he had. The plans no longer worked quite so well, but it was too much trouble to devise new ones. Anyhow, hadn't they always beaten the barbarians with those plans, and wouldn't they always beat them?

They found out differently.

Fighting began again—nothing much; just barbarians pushing against the Roman frontier, testing for soft spots. They found them, and the frontier drew in a little. The barbarians might be wild, but they were nobody's fools. They found out that the Romans weren't superior beings, and they pushed a little harder.

Rome was not worried. Times weren't quite as good as they had been, that was all. It was fantastic to imagine that painted savages might conquer Rome.

Then the frontier drew in a little more. The barbarians pushed a little harder. The invincible legions were beaten, and beaten again. They won some victories, too, but victories did not come easily.

Life went on in civilized Europe much as it had for time out of mind. After all, the barbarians were far away, and they could never break the iron ring of the legions. Rome, the city itself, was a little old-fashioned and out of date. There were really two Roman Empires now, one still centered in the old city and a newer, more vigorous one in Constantinople, the city of the Emperor Constantine, where Europe and Asia meet.

Finally, the capital of the Western Empire was moved to another city in Italy. Rome's greatness became a memory. But the Roman way of life would never change—that was as fixed as the stars.

So Tomasius Strabo thought. He was a landowner, partly Gallic and partly Roman—a descendant of old Quintus Rufinus—and he lived in a comfortable villa near where the city of Arles, France, is today. Tomasius was not as rich as his ancestors had been, but he had a good farm, and slaves to work it. It never occurred to him that things would change. And he was lucky. Things didn't change for him. Tomasius died in his bed, peacefully, looking out at his vineyards.

His son was not so lucky. He saw the legions crumble before the barbarians and watched them come swarming through the rich farmlands of Gaul. He died one bright August day in the year A.D. 480, and the last thing he saw was the edge of a battle-ax in the hand of a barbarian who belonged to the tribe of Franks.

He left a daughter, and she married a Frankish warrior, and their sons and grandsons played in the ruins of the Roman villa and never gave it another thought.

The old world was gone now. A barbarian king sat in Rome. The legions no longer marched. Roman law was forgotten, and gangs of cutthroats wandered over Europe. The roads were breaking up, but that didn't matter because people stayed pretty close to home. Where was there to go? There was no trade, no law, no money, no learning, no real authority except that of the Church, and even that was shaky.

Matters couldn't go on that way. Somebody had to step in and take charge, and sure enough, he came along—the Man on Horseback.

But where did he come from? The last we saw of the man on horseback, you remember, he was a light cavalryman, skirmishing and shooting his arrows. He hadn't amounted to much.

But things had changed. We mentioned a battle in which barbarian horsemen had smashed and routed Roman legions. With that battle, the cavalry moved to the center of the stage and held it for over a thousand years. After that battle, the Man on Horseback was the spearpoint of attack, the leader, the important part of any army.

In the old days the horseman couldn't accomplish much, for one simple reason: he had to fight sitting down. He could shoot a bow or wield a light weapon, but he had to pay so much attention just to staying on top of his horse that he couldn't do any really heavy fighting. That had to be left to the foot soldier.

Then, in the year A.D. 378, the Goths fought a Roman army at Adrianople, in what is now Turkey, and practically wiped them out because the Goths had an amazing new weapon. Not a sword or spear. Probably, in their blind panic, the Romans never noticed it. But what the Goths used on the battlefield that day doomed the heavy legions, changed history, and opened the door to the Knight in Armor.

The Goths rode with stirrups.

Does that sound trivial? Think a minute. With stirrups, a mounted man is secure in the saddle. He is no longer dependent on the shaky grip of his knees against the horse's barrel. He can't be pushed off easily.

Most important of all, he can fight standing up. He has something to brace himself against, a support which will let him put his whole weight behind the thrust of a lance or the swing of a sword. He can stand up to shocks and blows which would send a stirrup-less rider sprawling to the ground.

There are other advantages to stirrups. A man in heavy armor can mount a horse without having to be hoisted aboard like a keg of salt pork. He doesn't tire so easily. (Straddle a tree limb and let your legs hang down for an hour, if you want to see how much of an ache you can stand.)

It seems odd that it took so long before somebody thought of stirrups. They came from the Orient, like so many other notable inventions; and as usual, it took the Europeans to grasp what could really be done with them.

Of course stirrups did not change everything overnight. Many people clung stubbornly to the old ways. One of the last stands made by foot soldiers against mounted knights was at Hastings, England, in 1066: Norman knights against Saxon foot soldiers—and the Saxons nearly won, at that.

But from about the year 500, the mounted knight was firmly in the saddle in more ways than one. He lived in a rough, tough time, especially if he happened to be born in that stormy period we call the Dark Ages, between A.D. 500 and 1000. These were not the same as the Middle Ages. The two are often confused, but they are as different as midnight and dawn. The Dark Ages were mostly a period of lawlessness and confusion.

In the Dark Ages, most fighting men were no better than modern gangsters. During the earlier part of that period they were not really knights at all, because the system had not been worked out yet. A warrior of the Dark Ages was as far from the "gentil, parfit knight" of Chaucer's day (1380) as we are from Chaucer.

Men of the Dark Ages were neither gentil nor parfit; they were as tough as bear steak. Chronicles of the times—written by monks, the only ones who could write at all—are one long story of raids, treachery, slaughter, and robbery. They are full of old tales about heroes driving their enemies into a church and setting it afire, or melting lead and pouring it down someone's gullet.

Their never-ending wars made Western Europe a dismal wilderness for centuries. People were not quite so savage in Byzantium, the Eastern Roman Empire, which was still powerful, or in some of the Mohammedan countries. Or at least they were savage in a more refined way.

59

One of Sir Roger de Wyke's ancestors was a wild man of the Dark Ages. His name was Huberic Split-Chin, son of Clodalbert. His nickname was due to a trifling accident: when he was eight years old, a playmate hit him with an old spearhead. Huberic was a Frankish chieftain and he lived in the middle of the darkest of the Dark Ages, the seventh century A.D. His fortress-house, made of logs and surrounded by a palisade, stood in what is now west-central France. It looked for all the world like a pioneer blockhouse on our own frontier.

Huberic knew nothing about old General Strabo and wouldn't have cared to know. His life was much like that of an Iroquois chief at the time of the Pilgrim Fathers. Huberic had a few more tools, but not much more knowledge of the world at large, and probably not as much respect for law.

On the morning of his thirty-fourth birthday—a beautiful spring day in 637—Huberic felt gloomy because he was getting old, and sighed for his vanished youth at an age when men today are just beginning to get established.

He didn't know it, of course, but he was going to die that day.

Chapter 5: The Death of Huberic Split-Chin: A.D. 637

It was a small world Huberic lived in. Around his house was a clearing with pigs rooting in it. Close by were the huts of his people, and a little way off were the fields they tilled. Beyond them was pasture for cattle, sheep, and goats; then a river, which marked the end of Huberic's lands. And beyond that was a forest in which wolves howled.

Huberic had only the vaguest idea how far the forest stretched. For him, the world consisted of his own lands, the lands of his neighbors—with whom he quarreled endlessly—and the forest. A road went by, not far from Huberic's stronghold. It had been built by the Romans and was still in fairly good repair, although Huberic and his neighbors had taken many of the square paving stones for building purposes.

Sometimes caravans of traders came down this road. If they were too strong to be robbed, Huberic would let them go, and might even entertain them. From the traders he learned about cities, mountains, and oceans by hearsay. Once a priest read him some inscriptions carved on the piles of stones which lay scattered about—ruins of Roman buildings. The priest was greatly excited about them but Huberic was not much interested.

He was the lord of some two hundred draggletail peasants, most of whom lived almost within shouting distance of his big log house. He also had his personal gang of fifty Frankish warriors, who spent their days hunting, fighting, robbing, and drinking.

That was Huberic's world, and he was content with it. He knew that somewhere, far off to the northwest, lived a man who called himself King of the Franks, but Huberic had never heard from the king and rarely thought about him. Somewhat closer was a lord who was supposed to be Huberic's superior. He lived about fifty miles away, and every once in a while he sent tax-collectors to Huberic's holdings. They would drive away some pigs and cattle while Huberic cursed them. He didn't dare try to stop the tax men; the lord would have come down with his men-at-arms and burned Huberic's house, and Huberic knew it. But most of the time he left the lord alone, and the lord left him alone. This arrangement suited them both.

Huberic spent a good deal of his time fighting. He fought bandits, not because he wanted to uphold law and order, but because he wanted to hijack what they had stolen. He fought the wandering tribes that still came down from the north and west. He fought his neighbors, especially fat Balto the Earless, whose house was ten miles away through the woods. When nothing better offered, Huberic fought his wife, Thurhilda. It was a good life. He enjoyed it.

On his birthday Huberic got up with the sun, argued with Thurhilda for a while, dodged the wooden platter she threw at him, and went out of the dark, smelly house into the courtyard to confer with his trusted lieutenant, Ildebard.

He didn't notice the racket in the littered courtyard—scolding women, crowing roosters, squalling children. He was used to it, and besides, he had other things on his mind. This was the day he was going to take revenge on his unfriendly neighbor, Balto the Earless. Balto had been caught once by some of the Celtic natives who still lurked in remote parts of the Frankish forest. They had sent his ears back to his wife, with a message that his head would follow unless she sent a ransom. She had paid.

"They should have cut his fat throat," Huberic grumbled. Balto was getting to be a problem. Whenever Huberic thought of his fat neighbor, whose lack of ears was hidden by long braids of hair, he felt waves of anger. Balto always seemed to be one step ahead of him. They had started out holding about the same amount of land and the same number of peasants, but in ten years Balto had made himself master of twice as much land as Huberic had.

His system was to form a temporary alliance with one neighbor and then turn on another. Huberic himself had made such a pact with Balto a few years earlier. They had joined forces against a chieftain named Osbert. They had ended Osbert's career, but Balto had come out of the affair with the best farms and pastures and most of the cattle. Huberic got only some swampland, a few leagues of scrubby forest, and a herd of half-wild pigs. He still didn't understand it.

No, Balto was not a good neighbor. Besides, Huberic's cattle had been vanishing lately and he strongly suspected where they were going, in spite of Balto's bland denials. He had tried to follow Balto's example and form an alliance with another chieftain against the earless one, but his efforts had come to nothing. Huberic was a good fighter but not much of a diplomat, and in the end, the best revenge he could think of was to run off some of Balto's cattle. It was for such a raid he was headed today.

Ildebard met him in front of the gate which cut the high, palisaded wall. He grinned slyly, and tugged at his mustache with his right hand, from which two fingers were missing. "Just like I told you," he said. "Balto's left thirty fine cattle out in a meadow near the river. He's got no guard over them but an old man and a boy."

Huberic grunted. He liked the idea of taking the cattle, but it didn't sound like Balto to leave them practically unguarded.

Ildebard seemed to know what Huberic was thinking. "He'd have more guards around, except he's having trouble with old Hegemund, over on the other side of his lands," Ildebard said. "He's got to send men over there to ride the boundaries, and that leaves the door open for us. If you ask me—"

"I didn't ask you," Huberic growled. "You talk too much."

He stalked out of the gate. Fifteen more of his men were waiting. This was a lot of men to take on a cattle raid, but it was safer that way. Balto never went anywhere without at least ten men, and the thought of meeting him in some forest glade without having his own followers along made Huberic shudder. He did not expect a fight on this little expedition, but you never knew. War was always just behind the next tree.

Huberic's fighting costume was as different from Sir Roger's as it was from General Strabo's. His long woolen trousers were wrapped with the thongs from his rawhide brogans. A long-sleeved shirt reached to the middle of his thighs, over the trousers. The outfit made him look like nothing so much as a modern athlete in sweat-shirt and pants—but no coach would let his athletes put on anything quite so caked with dirt and sweat.

Huberic's armor consisted of a leather corselet, sleeveless, which laced up the sides. Strips of iron over his shoulders, and iron rings an inch in diameter across the front, protected his heart and stomach. On his head Huberic wore a steel cap. He was proud of the cap; not many minor chieftains owned one. It didn't fit him, and on mornings like this one, when his head was fuzzy from too much ale the night before, the steel cap gave him a headache. But it was a sort of badge of authority.

Wide leather bracelets studded with bronze protected his fore-arms. From his wide belt dangled his "francisc," or throwing-ax, which looked like a tomahawk. He could use it at close quarters, too. This, and the "scramasax," were the favorite Frankish weapons. The scramasax was a heavy, murderous single-edged knife with a long handle—actually a combination knife and short sword. Huberic had a long sword, too, but he left it behind. The steel was not good, and he had a hard time keeping it sharp. Besides, he felt more at home with francisc and scramasax. He was an expert with both. He also carried a spear, seven feet long with an iron head, and a round

shield about two feet in diameter, made of leather-covered wood, hung from his back.

His followers were similarly dressed and armed, but none of them had helmets. Some wore leather caps, and some only their own long hair, wound around their heads to act as protection. None of them possessed iron-studded corselets, although Ildebard had one covered with little plates of horn. But each carried a francisc—some had two—and a scramasax.

They were all mounted on horseback. The horses would have drawn a snort of contempt from Sir Roger, but Huberic was proud of them. He could ride well enough, although he was not at home in the saddle the way a knight of a later age had to be. He preferred to do his battling on foot, as his Frankish ancestors had. Nonetheless, the horses were more than a means of transportation to Huberic; they were a symbol of authority, like his steel cap. No one except a fighting man could hope to own a horse.

Huberic mounted and they rode off. Behind them, the ten-foot wooden gate swung shut, and Huberic's house was completely surrounded by a palisade of sharpened stakes. Watchmen stood guard on a platform behind the fence.

As the raiders wound through the fields, the laborers looked up but didn't stop their work. Every little while Huberic and his men passed an armed guard, who kept an eye open for possible attack and at the same time saw to it that the peasants didn't stand idle for even an instant. They passed the pasture land, entered the forest, and rode along a narrow track. Ildebard came up to ride beside Huberic. "We'll have those cattle back before Balto finds out anything about it. This is going to be an easy one, chief."

Huberic's qualms hadn't left him. "Sure. And he'll be over stealing my animals tomorrow."

"Not Balto!" said Ildebard. "He's in trouble with old Hegemund, right up to the place where his ears ought to be. And you know Hegemund. He's a sharp old devil. If Balto takes his men to come after us, why, Hege——"

"I know," Huberic interrupted impatiently. Ildebard was too full of talk today. Huberic knew all about Balto's quarrel with Hegemund; that was the only reason he had agreed to this raid in the first place. Now that he stopped to think about it, the whole thing had been Ildebard's idea.

They wound on through the forest. From time to time they passed through a clearing where a farm had stood—a clearing that was rapidly going back to woodland. Now and then a herd of frightened swine crashed away through the trees. There was no sign of human handiwork, barring an occasional half-buried flagstone which marked some old Roman road.

At last, far ahead, Huberic spied the glint of the little river which marked the limit of his property. He held up his spear, and the troop halted. Cautiously, he and Ildebard dismounted to scout ahead. "The cattle should be just over the river," Ildebard whispered. "I saw them yesterday." They peered through the trees. "There! Look!" He pointed.

The cattle were there, all right, grazing peacefully on a grassy patch. And as Ildebard had said, the only guards were a graybeard and a boy, both sound asleep.

"This is going to be easier than taking a bucket of ale from a kitchenmaid," whispered Ildebard. "We can't let those two get away to spread the alarm. We can ride up the river a half-mile and cross at the ford, where the old bridge used to be. Then we can come down from behind and drive the cattle right across the river."

Huberic scowled. He should be the one making the plans, not Ildebard. His lieutenant seemed to be taking the whole thing into his own hands. What he said was only common sense, and yet—a voice inside him whispered a warning. This was *too* easy! Even if Balto was fighting old Hegemund, he certainly had enough men-at-arms to put a guard over thirty fat cattle! And right on the borderline of Huberic's land, too. But as he watched the sleek beasts, Huberic's greed swelled. He could use those cows! Hadn't Balto stolen some of his best cattle, and then denied knowing anything about it? Two could play that game!

He slid backward into the trees. "Let's go," he said, and mounted.

The troop rode through the forest to the ford. A few slabs of stone showed where the Romans had maintained a bridge. Ildebard scouted ahead, and signaled back that all was clear, before Huberic led his men splashing through the shallow water.

Now they were in Balto's territory, and his nervousness increased. His men felt uneasy too. They crowded up closer, darting glances left and right, each one with spear or francisc ready. The horses' hoofs made no sound on the ancient carpet of leaves under the big trees. "We'll get far enough from the river to circle around behind them," Ildebard said in an undertone. "Then—" his hand with the missing fingers closed into a fist to show how the cattle would be caught.

The forest was too quiet. Something was wrong. The hairs on the back of Huberic's head prickled—a sure sign of danger. Then, from up ahead, sounded the moo of a cow, and Huberic thought greedily of the loot. After all, they were only just across the river from his own land. In another hour—

The forest dwindled to scrub. Ahead was an outcropping of granite, massive boulders scattered over the earth, some of them thirty feet high. Ildebard pointed. "We'll go around those, then—"

Huberic glanced at him sharply. Ildebard seemed nervous, more fidgety than he should be, and there was a queer gleam in his eyes. Huberic looked again at the scattered boulders, and the sense of danger swept over him like a wave.

Suddenly he knew.

He pulled back on his reins to turn the horse. At the same time he raised his spear. "Trap!" he roared. "Trap! Turn and run!"

His men milled, caught off guard. With a heave of his powerful arm Huberic threw his spear at Ildebard. It hit Ildebard's horse, which reared, throwing its rider. "Traitor! Dog!" Huberic yelled.

From behind the boulders poured a shouting mass of horsemen. In the bulky form of one of them, Huberic recognized Balto the Earless, wearing a scarlet tunic.

"Run!" Huberic shouted to his men. "Make for the river!" He sawed at his reins to turn the snorting horse. Before him, his panicky men fled toward the ford. He followed at a gallop.

A thrown francisc flashed past his head and bounced off the trunk of an oak. Balto was shouting hoarsely, urging his men on.

Huberic was filled with rage, partly at Balto, more at the treachery of Ildebard, but most of all at his own stupidity. He should have known it was a snare! To let Balto and that black hound Ildebard trick him so! They knew his greed for cattle and they had baited their trap.

He kicked his heels into the sides of the horse. The pursuers were coming up fast. Balto had good mounts. If only he could get to the ford! Actually, he didn't know what he could do when he got to the ford. Balto wouldn't stop there. But all Huberic could think was: Get over the river! Get back on my own side!

There was the water, the shattered bridge. Some of his men were already pushing their horses into the river, throwing up showers of spray. Behind him, Balto was still bellowing.

Then Huberic's horse stumbled. It tried to gallop again, unevenly, and slowed down, limping. Frantic, Huberic kicked it. No use. The horse had hit its leg against one of the mossy, cracked squares of marble left from the Roman bridge. Very lame now, it stumbled again, nearly pitching Huberic over its neck.

Balto's men howled. Snarling, Huberic slid to the ground and ran over to put his back against the thick trunk of a tree. His francisc was balanced in his hand, ready for hurling.

The pursuers reined in. Balto came forward, a grin on his heavy face. "Let the others go," he ordered. "We'll catch them later. This one is the man I want." He laughed. "Where are all your cattle, Huberic Split-Chin?"

Huberic's francisc whirled through the air, and the fat chieftain caught it on his shield. It stuck there. Balto laughed again. Huberic snapped his scramasax from his belt and stood at bay. He had no hope of rescue. Some of his men had already surrendered, and the others soon would. They would just as soon serve Balto as Huberic. Sooner—Balto was shrewder. Balto would never have led them into a trap. Red rage took possession of Huberic.

"Get down and fight, you fat bladder, you tub of guts, you cowardly pile of tripe!" he roared.

Balto, still smiling, made a gesture. A francisc hurtled through the air. Huberic dodged. "Get off that horse and fight like a man, pig-belly!" he shouted again.

One of Balto's men, eager for a fight or for glory, slid from his horse and ran toward Huberic, holding his spear over one shoulder

ready for a thrust. Huberic crouched. When the spear leaped forward he dodged it expertly, fell on one knee, and gave a savage cut
with his scramasax.

The man-at-arms, one leg nearly severed, howled and fell. **Huberic**

jumped forward and brought the blade of his heavy weapon down on the man's neck. The howl ended. Huberic grabbed up the spear.

"Next one!" he jeered. "Come on!" In the excitement of battle he had almost forgotten that his life was measured only by minutes.

Balto looked down at the fallen man. "Clumsy," he said mildly. "I told you Huberic was tough. Stupid, but tough." He glanced around at his followers. "Go get him."

The men dismounted and formed a half-circle around Huberic, who still crouched with his back to the tree. Spears ready, they walked warily forward.

Huberic's mind cleared of its red tide of rage. He knew that in a few heartbeats he would die. Somehow it didn't seem to matter. Then, suddenly, it mattered very much. In place of the rage came black fear. He gave a wild yell and lunged forward, trying to break through the circle of warriors. His captured spear flailed wildly. Two of Balto's men were down. He'd make it yet!

Something like a blow from a club hit him in the back. He was lying on the ground, staring at a squared piece of marble a few inches from his eyes. The marble bore carved letters, mossy and worn with age: "IMP CAES TIB ..." Huberic knew they were letters, and it seemed important to him. "Romans," his dying mind said. "I wonder if—"

And that was all. The Romans, the forest, the treachery of Idlebard, Balto's grinning face—everything melted together and vanished.

The fat chieftain stood looking down at Huberic's body. All had come out just as he planned. He had known Huberic would not be able to resist the lure of cattle. And with Ildebard's help it had been almost too easy. The rest of his men would come up soon, and they would all ride on to Huberic's stronghold. By nightfall he would have added Huberic's land, and Huberic's spearmen, to his own. Then let old Hegemund look out!

72

Ildebard limped up, smiling, and stood beside Balto's stirrup. "It all worked out just as you said, Balto. I didn't have any trouble at all leading him here. Huberic was a simple fool."

Balto looked down at him, and his grin faded slowly. "Yes. A simple fool. A good fighting man, but a fool. I think, Ildebard, that you would have a little more trouble betraying me." His voice was icy.

"But, my lord—" Suddenly panic looked out of Ildebard's eyes. "But, my lord, I never would betray you! You know it was only because I—"

"You're quite right," Balto said. "You will never betray me, Ildebard." His francisc flashed. Ildebard, his head split, sank beside the body of the man he had led to death.

One of Balto's men gave a sudden cackle of nervous laughter, then stopped with a gulp.

Thoughtfully, Balto looked down at the two bodies. "A tough fool and a traitor," he said. "Take that helmet of Huberic's. I can use it." He turned briskly. "Get to your horses. We have work to do."

He rode away toward the ford.

Huberic's young son got away from Balto, and escaped through the woods. He fled north and put himself under the protection of Count Grimald. Balto didn't worry about him. He had other fish to fry.

The quarrel between Balto and old Hegemund broke out with renewed fury. For once, Balto had met an enemy stronger and wilier than he was. Balto was killed, and Hegemund became the most powerful landholder in the district. By some miracle, he died a natural death. His two sons fought over which one would get his acres. Their serfs rebelled against both of them. Then Count Grimald came down with an army and took over the whole property, but he got into a war with another count, and everything fell to pieces again.

All over Western Europe at that time, this was the pattern of events. Kings of the Franks came and went, each one a little weaker than the last. Nobody paid any attention to them. A strong man would rise up and bring comparative peace and quiet to a district; then he would die, and the dismal fighting would begin again.

It couldn't last. Some kind of government had to be established, to bring a measure of security to a lawless world. It came, carried by the man on horseback—the Knight in Armor—and it was called the Feudal System.

Nowadays we use the word "feudal" to mean hopelessly out-of-date, cruel, barbaric; to describe a system which holds people in helpless slavery. And the feudal system was cruel and barbaric, in part; but it was also the salvation of the Western World, and in its beginnings was hailed with delight as new and progressive.

Feudalism was a combination of customs borrowed from the wrecked Roman world and from the German tribal system which took its place. The whole gaudy show of knights and squires, ladies fair, heraldry, tournaments, trials by combat, and all the rest had its roots in the desperate need of the people to have someone to protect them.

That was the job of the armored knight.

He was created to protect his "vassals," the people under him—tradesmen, craftsmen, farmers. In return for his protection, they gave him service, or paid him rent, or handed over some of the things they produced.

The knight was protected by a nobleman, who was protected by a still greater nobleman, who was protected by the king. And each one, to pay for the protection, gave something to the one who protected him. Everybody was happy—at least in theory.

Of course it didn't work out as neatly as that. The man on horseback wasn't nearly so interested in protecting people as he was in getting them to work for him.

And as long as he had a lance and a sword and a big horse, the knight figured he might as well use them. So the knights and barons were forever going on expeditions, stirring up fights with other knights and barons in order to steal their land. Worst of all, they kept calling on their peasants to lay down their hayforks and follow them into battle.

Was such a state of affairs any better than having no government at all? It was—considerably. At the very least, it *was* a government, with laws and rules and some pretense at justice. Your lord *did* try to protect you, if only to keep somebody else from claiming you. Knights and men-at-arms *did* work at keeping down outlaws. Each noble and knight was personally interested in seeing that farmers got good crops, merchants made a profit, and craftsmen turned out quality goods.

It wasn't long, though, before a peculiar notion began to take hold of the Men on Horseback—and their women. The notion was that they were beings of a finer, higher nature than mere peasants or traders. Instead of being just protectors of the land and the people on it, they became owners of the land—and the people on it. They thought of themselves as being of "gentle blood," and of everyone else as being of "base blood." Of course, "gentle" did not mean at all what it means now, kind and soft-hearted. It meant high-born. If you were gentle, you were Somebody.

The Men on Horseback formed a sort of fraternity among themselves, an exclusive club. They were held together by the vows and rules of knighthood. They called it "chivalry," which is just another way of saying Man on Horseback. In Germany, the knight was a *Ritter* or rider, and in Spain he was a *caballero*, another way of saying horseman. (It's odd that of all the languages, English is the only one that doesn't use a word meaning horseman. "Knight" comes from an old word meaning servant.)

Not every man of gentle blood became a knight, and there were many cases when a base-born man of exceptional ability did achieve this honor. But, in general, a boy followed in the footsteps of his father.

It was a pleasant arrangement, for the gently-born. And gradually they began to look on work with disdain. The thought horrified them—work was for peasants. A knight's business was fighting. War was his reason for living. War was his work, his play, his pleasure. If he wasn't fighting, he was pretending to, in tournaments or at the chessboard.

Very early in the game, those who were successful in the business of fighting began to patch together little pieces of land into bigger ones, in much the same way as old Hegemund did. They promised to protect a weaker neighbor if he would swear loyalty to them. Sometimes they simply moved in and took over. Slowly, the weaker ones were dispossessed and the strong ones got stronger.

The little pieces of land (and land was the only thing that mattered) continued to grow into bigger ones. Counties and dukedoms and kingdoms began to appear. For centuries the boundary lines shifted back and forth like pieces of glass in a kaleidoscope. In time, real countries took shape, more or less along the lines of the countries we know today. Of course, this is the sketchiest possible outline of the way the small barbarian holdings grew, through the feudal

system, into great nations like France, Spain, and Germany. It was a far more complicated process than this. But the point is that during the centuries when nations were slowly forming, the people who did most of the forming were the knights, the Men on Horseback.

A lot of romantic nonsense has been written about the Knight in Shining Armor: unselfish, brave, courteous, a sort of Eagle Scout who thought of nothing but rescuing fair damsels in distress and helping the downtrodden. Did you ever see the famous picture of Sir Galahad by the English artist Sir Edward Burne-Jones—Galahad, whose strength was as the strength of ten because his heart was pure?

There were a good many selfless, dedicated knights, pure in thought and deed, brave, reverent, and courteous. Godfrey of Bouillon, for one, a leader of the First Crusade. The Chevalier Bayard, for another, who lived in the twilight of knighthood, nearly five hundred years after Godfrey. St. Louis, king of France, although he was hardly a fighting man. Sir John Chandos. Bertrand du Guesclin. William Marshal of England, perhaps the greatest fighting man who ever wore armor—a steadfast, honorable, brave knight who was still swinging a sword at an age when most men can do nothing but sit by a fire.

But we are getting ahead of our story. Slowly, slowly, through the Dark Ages, some measure of order returned to Europe. A few more traders ventured on the roads. Peasants had a slightly better chance of getting their crops harvested before somebody burned them. A few scholars began to appear—monks, many of them from the remote country of Ireland, who kept some learning alive. Craftsmen in stone, in metal, and in wood began to do work which was considerably less barbaric than it had been.

In the beginning, the feudal system brought a little security. Not much, but a great deal more than the poor harassed people had been used to. Counts kept barons in line, barons kept smaller landholders in line, and so on down.

In Gaul, or Frankland, the king had little real authority. But the kings of the Franks had a series of right-hand men who were strong, able, and tough. They were called Mayors of the Palace; they were the real rulers, and Western Europe owes a great deal to them.

When the Moors of Africa, who had conquered Spain, crossed the mountains into France, a certain Charles, then Mayor of the Palace, gathered his Franks together and threw out the invaders in a terrible battle that changed history.

(Huberic's great-great-grandson took part in that battle of Tours, in the year 732. For thirty years afterward he bored people with his stories of how he had beaten the Moors almost single-handed. Finally he began to believe it himself.)

Charles won the name of "The Hammer," and that is how he is known to history—Charles Martel. His son, Pepin, weary of being only a hired hand for a useless king, threw the king out and put on the crown.

Pepin's son was one of the great men of all time. He was named Charles, for his grandfather, and won the title of Charles the Great —Charlemagne. Under him, Frankland began to look less like a patchwork quilt and more like a country. He made the counts and barons fight for him instead of against each other. Charlemagne spent most of his long reign fighting, and he built up a formidable army.

Under Charlemagne, the Man on Horseback really came into his own. The main striking force of his army was made up of horsemen. Most of them were gentle-born. It is still too early to call them knights; there was some sort of ceremony when they were made warriors, perhaps girding on a sword, but all the glitter of chivalry and knight-errantry was still far in the future. The idea was there, though.

Charlemagne's heavy cavalry was called "caballarii," which means "horsemen." A caballarius wore an iron helmet, carried a round shield, and slung a straight sword at his side. The helmet was a simple iron hat. His hauberk was made of iron rings or iron scales, sewed overlapping on a leather tunic. This scale armor was called "jazerant," and was good protection but miserably hot and heavy. A caballarius carried a lance, although he didn't use it as knights would in another two centuries; he still held it like a spear. He might carry the old-fashioned francisc, still a good weapon, or a scramasax.

Charlemagne fought the Moors in Spain, the Lombards in Italy, and the Saxons in Germany. He was crowned Emperor of the Romans in 800, when he was fifty-eight years old. People thought of him as being the same kind of Roman Emperor as Trajan or Marcus Aurelius had been, centuries before. He wasn't, of course. The world had changed too much. But Charlemagne was without doubt the most powerful monarch in Europe, and to his faithful caballarii he was the most powerful ruler in the world.

To one of them, a young man named Rolf, the emperor was almost a god. Rolf was the great-grandson of that descendant of Huberic's who had fought at Tours. In the year 801, Rolf went with the Emperor's army across the mountains into Spain.

This land south of the great mountains was not nearly so pleasant as Frankland. It was hotter, drier, more barren, cut by deep ravines and studded with huge rocks. The people were wilder, too—as shy as hares, and dirt-poor.

Young Rolf missed the carpet of tall grass, the cool forests, and sparkling streams of Frankland. But not for the world would he have let Haldegar know of his homesickness. Haldegar would only have laughed. Rolf idolized the tough warrior, twice his age, who had served the great Emperor for twenty years and who was never surprised or dismayed by anything.

There were other things to think about besides homesickness. Haldegar, Rolf, and six foot soldiers were scouting down a valley to see if they could find any trace of the Moorish horsemen who had been harassing the Frankish army. Of course Haldegar, the caballarius, was in command. Theoretically Rolf was his second-in-command; but he knew, as well as any of the foot soldiers did, that he had been sent along merely to watch and learn. He was only eighteen, but after all he was the second son of Count Alferic, gently-born, and destined to command some day.

The Franks, under Louis, son of the great Charles, and Count William of Toulouse, were on their way to the town of Barcelona. So far, the only battles had been with the wild Spanish mountaineers and small forces of Moors. And they hadn't been battles, exactly—just skirmishes. But as Haldegar said, "You can't ever tell with

Moors. We might turn a corner and come face to face with fifty thousand of them."

Rolf didn't really believe him, but it was an exciting thought and it kept him peering from side to side as they marched slowly down the dry river bed which was the valley floor. On each side, hills rose steeply, dotted with boulders, covered with clumps of dry grass. Once or twice Rolf saw a movement on the hills and his heart jumped, but a second look always revealed a family of wild sheep before he had made a fool of himself by sounding the alarm.

The soldiers were old campaigners like Haldegar. They slouched along easily, muttering among themselves. Rolf had an uneasy feeling that they looked on him with amused contempt, and as a result he tried to carry himself with the same half-bored casualness as the caballarii.

They turned a bend, and Rolf's expectancy sagged. Instead of fifty thousand Moors, there was nothing in sight but more dry river bed, with a patch of scraggly forest a half-mile or so ahead.

Haldegar, turning in his saddle, said partly to Rolf and partly to the men: "We'll go up past those trees, then turn. If there aren't any Moors—and there won't be—we'll go back."

Rolf nodded, and big Gerlund, leader of the foot soldiers, grunted assent. Now that he had broken the silence, Haldegar apparently felt like talking, and he began to tell about the Emperor's first venture into Spain more than twenty years before. Charles had been only King then, not Emperor, and Haldegar a youngster of nineteen, much like Rolf was now.

"This country hasn't changed," Haldegar said. "Crazy then, crazy now. Half Christian, half infidel, and I think the Christians are worse than the Moors. Every last one of 'em savages. Remember, Gerlund?"

The big foot soldier remembered, all right, and the two men spent a few minutes recalling the long-ago campaign. Charlemagne's expedition had been a failure, and the army had finally trooped back across the Pyrenees.

"Wasn't that when the Moors attacked the army, and Count Hruodlund held them off until the Emperor could get back?" Rolf asked timidly.

Haldegar gave a bark of laughter. "Oh, they're making too much of that, now," he said. "What happened was that Hruodlund of Brittany got himself bushwhacked and killed by a troop of these mountaineers. It was his own fault, at that. But he was the Emperor's friend, and Charles has been itching to get back ever since."

"Why did he wait twenty years?"

"He's been busy." Haldegar chuckled. "Oh, old Charles has had plenty to do. I've followed him, youngster, into Germany and Italy, over half the world. But he never forgets. Charles never forgets anything."

The caballarius lapsed into silence again, and Rolf began thinking of the Emperor, whom he had seen only once, in the capital at Aix-la-Chapelle—a grand, bearded figure on a huge black horse.

It was hot and still in the hidden valley. High overhead the birds wheeled. The horses' hoofs were almost soundless on the ground, a thin crust of baked mud over the sand of the dry river bed. The trees were closer, a patch of pines perhaps ten acres in extent, coming down into the valley. In spring, Rolf knew, water from the storms in the mountains roared through this canyon, but now there was only an occasional patch of moisture.

Nothing stirred. It was almost, Rolf thought, like one of those enchanted lands the poets told about, a land where everything had been brought under a spell, so that—

Haldegar uttered a peculiar choking sound and swayed in his saddle. There was a flash of movement among the trees. Something whirred past Rolf, and Gerlund shouted.

Moors! The Moors were upon them! Rolf pulled his shield around and spurred up beside Haldegar. The caballarius stared at him with wide eyes, his mouth opening and closing. The shaft of an arrow stuck out of his throat, and blood was pumping from the wound.

"Get—go—" he muttered thickly; then a fountain of blood burst from his mouth, and he fell. One foot remained caught in a stirrup as his frightened horse bounded away.

I'm in command, Rolf thought, dazed. I have to tell the foot soldiers what to do. But in a flash of panic it occurred to him he didn't know what to do. And already the foot soldiers were beginning to run.

Another arrow plunged into the ground at his feet. His horse snorted and shied.

What would the Emperor do? What would Count William do? What would Haldegar have done? Run? It was unthinkable! Scurry back to the army and tell them a couple of arrows had come out of a thicket and a caballarius of the Emperor had turned tail? He wheeled his horse, fighting the animal's pull at the bridle. The soldiers were scattering, except Gerlund, who crouched behind his shield and shouted at the others to come back.

"I'll rally them," Rolf said. He spurred, and his horse bounded forward. "Get back!" he yelled, waving his lance. "Back, you cowards!"

One dodged him, cursing. Another tripped and fell. Rolf rode ahead of them, turned, and tried to round them up as a sheep dog rounds up sheep. Either because their panic was ebbing or they were ashamed, the soldiers slowed their flight and stopped.

"Running like rabbits from a couple of arrows!" Rolf stormed. "I thought you were soldiers!" He spurred back toward the patch of trees. "Come on, now. They've killed Haldegar. Are you going to let them boast that they killed a soldier of the Emperor and lived to tell of it?"

Gerlund still crouched behind his round shield, in which an arrow was now sticking. As Rolf rode up, Gerlund said, "There aren't very many of them. At least not very many with bows. There might be as many as a hundred without bows."

"A hundred!" one of the soldiers echoed. "What chance have we got against a hundred men?"

Rolf felt angry, excited, and confused all at once. Gerlund and the others were staring at him, and there was a look in Gerlund's eye that Rolf didn't like.

"Best take it easy, son," Gerlund said. "Haldegar's dead, and there's no sense in the rest of us ending up here too. We'll go back, easy-like, and tell 'em there's a strong body of Moors here. They'll send out a force to destroy 'em."

"Gerlund's right," a soldier said. "We're a scouting party, not an attacking force."

Anger overcame Rolf. "As long as we have one man left, we're an attacking force! I'm riding into those trees, and you spread out and follow. If there are too many, we'll retreat. But first we'll find out." He waved his lance and shouted, "Follow me!"

Not a soldier stirred. One shook his head and muttered. For a moment Rolf felt helpless. What should he do? Sit here and argue? Give in, and lead the retreat? Use his lance on their cowardly backs? He knew Haldegar would not have done any of those things. Haldegar would have ordered them to do whatever he wanted them to, and they would have obeyed without argument.

He clenched his teeth, turned the horse, and galloped toward the trees. "Follow me!" he shouted again.

Never had he felt so alone. He dared not look back to see if they were following. In a minute he would be in the trees, among— among what? A hundred Moorish soldiers?

Underbrush crackled beneath the horse's hoofs. A man jumped up before him, whirling an ax. As Rolf poised his lance, he saw that the man was no Moor. The ax whacked against his shield; then his lance drove home and was wrenched from his hand as the attacker fell.

He drew his sword. Other men were running toward him, dark men in leather or sheepskin. They held axes or short spears. Shouting gibberish, they formed a ring around his horse and jabbed at him with the spears.

Rolf spurred ahead, cut down one and shoved another aside with his shield. A point grated across the scales of his armor. Hands grabbed at his belt. Rolf cut, parried, and thrust, and all the time something deep inside him was thinking, in a detached, calm way: This is me, Rolf. I'm here, fighting. I've always wanted to be a warrior, and now I am one. These men want to kill me!

He felt a strong tug, lost his balance, and crashed to the ground. The howls of his attackers grew louder. One of them fell across him. Rolf shoved him off and tried to get to his knees. Something clanged against his helmet and waves of blackness clouded his eyes. When he came to himself, he was on one knee, swinging the sword he had managed to keep. The men in leather howled and hopped in front of him, poking with their spears or darting in to swing an ax.

No one told him what to do. He simply did it, keeping the sword flailing, standing off the attackers, who pressed in ever more closely. It couldn't last, and Rolf knew it.

Then there was an uproar amidst the trees, and he heard Gerlund's bellow.

The soldiers dashed in headlong, their swords reaching out like the tongues of snakes, the sharp bosses on their shields clawing at the men in leather. Under the sudden assault, the barbarians broke. They were no match for the battle-wise soldiers of the Emperor.

Rolf, still dizzy, hauled himself to his feet and shook his head. Sounds of battle echoed from the trees. He shouted and dashed toward the fighting. Gerlund and the others were running after the fleeing barbarians. They were outnumbered three to one, but they cared nothing for that. Rolf chased a young man clutching an ax, who darted from one tree to another, looking back with scared eyes. The Franks were howling like demons, and it was that, as much as anything, which had frightened the attackers.

They came to an open space—the barbarbians' camp, apparently, for Rolf saw cooking fires and a great heap of bags and bundles. A dozen or so women and a little cluster of ragged children huddled together, sobbing and screaming in fright.

The men, about fifteen of them, formed a line in front of their families and turned, desperate and at bay. Unarmored, poorly armed, they could not hope to stand against the Emperor's men.

Gerlund laughed. "All right, boys. Slow and easy. One at a time and finish 'em all off!"

Rolf grabbed his arm. "No, hold! Stop!"

The big soldier looked at him. "Stop? What for?"

"We won't kill them," Rolf said stubbornly. "Let them go."

Gerlund snarled, "Let them go? The ones who killed Haldegar? By the looks of them, they're the same kind that wiped out Count Hruodlund and the rear guard in '78. They're no good as prisoners."

"I said let them go," Rolf repeated.

An angry mutter came from the soldiers. Gerlund shook his head as if he could hardly believe what he was hearing. "Listen, son," he said, "stand aside. You've been hit on the head and it's addled your wits."

Rolf's head *was* aching, but his mind was perfectly clear. The barbarians stood defiantly, obviously scared to death but holding their primitive weapons ready for a hopeless defense. Behind them, the women and children moaned feebly and hopelessly. Rolf didn't try to analyze why he was determined to stop the slaughter; he knew only that he could not let Gerlund and the others loose with their swords among these frightened, helpless people.

90

"I'm a caballarius of the Emperor's army," he said steadily. "Don't call me 'son' any more, Gerlund. And I say we let these people live. I won't argue with you. There's no more to be said."

Gerlund drew back as if in amazement. "Well, now! Here's a piglet thinks it's a boar! A caballarius of the Emperor's army! Why, I was lugging a spear across Germany while you were squalling in a wet clout!" He raised his spear to striking position. "Now, son, get out of my way!" He tried to push Rolf aside.

Rolf raised his sword and dealt Gerlund a savage slap across the face with the flat of it. The soldier's head snapped back and he staggered. Then he snarled and drew back his arm. This time the spear was pointed straight at Rolf.

"Drop it," Rolf said calmly, "or I'll kill you."

Gerlund was a half a head taller and thirty pounds heavier. For a breath, the two stood glaring at each other, poised spear against pointed sword. Then the spear wavered and fell.

"I don't want to hurt you," Gerlund muttered.

"You won't," Rolf said. Something inside him whispered: All you have to do is show them who's in command and make them believe it. Why, it's easy! He felt calm and sure of himself. "We didn't come to kill miserable sheepherders," he said. "We came to find Moors. Count William wants these people on our side." He gestured with the sword. "Now move back."

The Franks shuffled back a few feet. One of them scowled and spat, but the others obeyed without hesitation. Gerlund stood for a minute, then moved back with the others.

Rolf turned. The barbarbians stood open-mouthed, watching the mad Franks. They hadn't the slightest idea of what was going on; probably they thought they were being taken prisoners. They were a wretched crew, dirty, ragged, and smelly.

"Do any of you speak our tongue?" Rolf asked.

One of the barbarians made a movement, and Rolf walked toward him. "I speak—one word, two words."

"Good." Rolf spoke slowly. "We will not hurt you. Why did you shoot arrows at us?"

The sheepherder wrinkled his forehead. "Afraid. We think—" He gestured and used some word which Rolf translated as "robbers."

"We come with the good Emperor of the Franks," Rolf said. "We will not hurt you. We are going to fight the dark-skinned men. The Moors. Are there any Moors near here?"

He had to repeat that several times and piece out the words with signs, but at last the barbarian nodded, jabbered with his fellows, and said: "Not any. Not close." He pointed. "Many dark-skin men there. Two day, three day."

He did not know how many, but made a wide gesture and chattered when Rolf pressed him. The barbarians were getting over their terror. They came crowding close, talking. The children were clinging to their fathers' legs, gazing round-eyed at the strangers. Even the women came forward, hesitatingly. One or two of the girls were pretty, in an unkempt sort of way. One, with enormous brown eyes, giggled and hid her round face as he looked. He ignored her, but he couldn't help a glow of satisfaction.

Rolf turned to the men. "You heard what this fellow said. No Moors closer than two or three days' travel. We'll go back and report. Gerlund, take a man and find Haldegar's body. You will ride his horse back."

Gerlund opened his mouth but said nothing, merely shrugged. He motioned to one of his comrades, and they disappeared. Rolf pointed to another. "You. Get my horse." The Frank moved off obediently.

Then Rolf pointed at the Spaniard. "You tell them that if they see Moors, come tell Emperor's men. The man who comes will be rewarded. Get good things."

When this had been translated—apparently it took ten times as many words in the barbarians' language as in Frankish—the sheep-herders grinned and nodded.

"And don't shoot at Frankish soldiers any more," Rolf added sternly. "Next time we kill!" He made a gesture of a throat being cut, and the men looked anxious. A couple of the women wailed. Rolf turned and walked away.

Silently the other Franks trooped after him. The soldier came up with his horse, and Rolf mounted. Gerlund met them outside the little forest with Haldegar's body slung over his saddle.

"All right," Rolf said crisply, "let's get back." His voice surprised him. It held a new note of authority, the voice of command. Gerlund was looking up at him. No longer did the half-hidden amusement flicker in his eyes. Neither, Rolf saw, was there any hostility, in spite of the red welt which still lay across Gerlund's cheek. Suddenly the old soldier grinned.

"You'll get along, son—I mean, Rolf," he said. "It took courage to go alone into those trees. I wouldn't have done it."

Rolf shrugged, trying to keep a smile of triumph from his face. "It had to be done."

"But I don't know why you wouldn't let us take revenge for Halde-gar. Show too much mercy to these barbarians, and none of us will be safe."

"Oh, nonsense!" Rolf knew that now he didn't have to explain, but for some reason he wanted to. "Do you suppose we have anything to fear from those people? Think, Gerlund. They're on our side now. Besides—"

Rolf struggled with an idea that had come to him, back there in the forest. The idea had something to do with the uselessness of killing for the sake of killing, and distaste for attacking the helpless, and the need for protecting women and children. He couldn't explain it. He would have to think it out for himself before trying to put it into words. Rolf didn't know it, but what he was trying to express was the idea that would come to be known as chivalry. But it would be some time yet before men adopted it, and Rolf was still half-barbarian himself.

"Besides—" Gerlund prompted.

"Oh, never mind," Rolf said. "Hurry up. We have to get back to the army with our report."

"Yes, sir," the big soldier said.

Charlemagne was a very great man. So great that after he died, the lesser men who followed him could not hold his vast empire together. Things went to pieces again. They were not quite so bad, perhaps, as they had been in the days of Huberic, but bad enough.

People began to talk wistfully of the good old days under Charlemagne. As always, the good old days got better and better with the passing of time, and the stories got bigger and bigger. When Rolf died in 847—he was a count by then—the great Emperor was already a legend, and men were telling stories about him that Rolf knew were not true, although he was too wise to say so.

One of the favorite stories was about Roland, one of Charlemagne's paladins, or heroes. Rolf knew all about Roland. On the day of his adventure with the sheepherders in the little forest, Haldegar had been talking about him, just before the arrow struck his throat.

Roland was really Hruodlund, the Count of Brittany who had been trapped by the mountaineers. The Spaniards were angry because Charlemagne's army had destroyed their town, and so they attacked the Frankish rear guard and cut them to pieces.

On that flimsy basis was erected one of the most famous legends of all time. The tribe of mountaineers became a horde of Moors. The minor skirmish became an epic battle. Hruodlund became Roland, the Perfect Hero, the Perfect Knight, instead of the hairy half-barbarian he actually was. Two or three hundred years later, Hruodlund himself would not have realized that he was the man they were talking about. In Italy they called him Orlando, and in Spain they called him Roldan. And the poets made up enough adventures about him to have kept poor Hruodlund busy for a dozen lifetimes— all because of a fight that resembled nothing so much as a party of Cheyennes attacking a wagon train.

The same thing happened with the most famous of all the knightly heroes, King Arthur of England. Arthur is a far more shadowy figure than Charlemagne. Most historians admit that someone existed who was the basis for the Arthur legends, but they don't know who he was, when he lived, or what he did. "Arthur" may be the composite of a half-dozen different men.

Most likely the original Arthur was a Celtic chieftain of the fifth or sixth century A.D. who rallied the tribes in Britain to fight the Saxon invaders of the island, after the Romans had pulled their legions out. He may have been a Roman, or a Celt trained in Roman methods of warfare. Or a general, or a "dux bellorum"—war chief— or even a real king. In those days, anyone who held a patch of ground bigger than a modern football field set himself up as a king.

Whoever Arthur was, his fighting men were not knights. They did not wear plate armor, or live in stone castles, or know anything about chivalry. Probably they were Celtic warriors, armed with spears and axes, who spoke a language something like modern Welsh. They doubtless remembered Roman customs, and may have lived in the crumbling ruins of the cities the Romans had built.

But Sir Lancelot, Sir Gawaine, Sir Tristram de Lyonesse, Elaine the Lily Maid of Astolat, and all the rest are—sad to say—pure fiction. They did, however, represent the knightly ideal. People who lived in the twelfth and thirteenth centuries liked to hear tales about knightly adventures and romance, and there were plenty of troubadours willing to furnish them. They remembered the old tales about Arthur, and brought them up to date—it would never do to have Sir

98

Lancelot pictured as a shaggy-haired barbarian with his face tattooed blue. So the legends, founded on scraps of history and well-seasoned with ancient folk tales, became tremendously popular.

But to get back to Charlemagne: Some years after he died, the Franks found they had a new terror to face—the Norsemen.

In chilly, rocky Scandinavia, far up in the north of Europe, people still held to the old ways. They were pagans. They knew nothing about the feudal system or knighthood. But one thing they did know, and know well: how to fight.

When their homeland began to get crowded, some of them put out to sea. They were delighted to find that the pickings were much better in France and Spain and Italy than in their own north country. When they got back they spread the news, and other eager Norsemen joined them. They descended southward like a plague. Year after year, they swept down on the richer countries of Europe, robbing and burning. "From the fury of the Norsemen, O Lord, deliver us!" prayed the people of France and Spain. "Fury" was a fitting word.

The Norsemen were as tough a people as ever lived. They were not afraid to be killed in battle; they looked forward to it, because if they died in a fight they were sure of an honored place in Valhalla, the Norse heaven. Their idea of heaven was a place where there was nothing to do but fight, drink, and eat—pleasures to be enjoyed in the order named.

The favorite Norse weapon was a battle-ax, a fearful thing five feet long, heavy enough to split a man in two. They had other weapons, of course, and they were uncommonly good at using them. The Norsemen wielded swords, heavy spears, and bows, all equally well. Chiefs and wealthy men wore a "byrnie," or short mail hauberk, but most were content with a leather jerkin or a woolen tunic. They might throw the skin of a bear or a wolf over their shoulders.

Sometimes they went mad with battle frenzy, threw off their clothes, and fought naked. Then they were called Berserkers, which means something like "bare-shirts," and even their friends were afraid of them. Modern doctors think the Berserkers got that way through eating a certain mushroom which drove them out of their minds for a while.

The Norsemen, though, didn't need mushrooms to be terrible enemies. In their "snekkjas," or dragon boats, they sailed light-heartedly over seas on which other people hardly dared to venture. They came to North America, probably many times—remember Leif Ericson? A band of Norsemen pushed down through the Baltic Sea and became the rulers of Russia. Norsemen also showed up at the court of the emperor of Byzantium in Constantinople, and became his personal bodyguards.

They were a remarkable people. Savages they may have been. Pirates, robbers, and mischief-makers they certainly were. It is curious to think that today the Danes, Swedes, and Norwegians are among the most peace-loving people on earth. Their ancestors were anything but that.

Every spring the dragon ships poked their ugly snouts out of the fjords. And every spring, from Ireland to North Africa, bells tolled and frightened people fled.

Every fall the dragon ships sailed back to the Northland, loaded down with the treasures of the world. Not all of them came back, of course. Some were sunk in battle, or by storms. And besides, the crews of some dragon ships just decided to stay away. They liked France or Spain or Ireland better than their own foggy birthplace, and they settled down in these lands. When they did that, the Norsemen showed that they were something more than mere barbarian raiders.

Norsemen conquered part of Ireland, founded the city of Dublin (the Irish Celts could never see the sense of cities), and set up a trading center there.

They invaded Britain in three great waves, and in the end took over the island completely. The first time was at the beginning of the Dark Ages, when they were opposed by King Arthur. These were not really Norsemen, but Saxons, their first cousins. Three hundred years later, after the Saxons were firmly established in England, the Danes came; they had to battle against King Alfred, but finally settled down more or less peaceably.

Finally, some descendants of the Norsemen came back in 1066, and took over England for good and all. They were called Normans then, but they were the same people. The name "Norman" had been given to Viking raiders who sailed up the rivers of France, liked what they saw, and stayed. They had made a treaty with the king of the Franks, married Frankish girls, and started a race in which the courage and energy of the Scandinavians were combined with the skill and tradition of the Franks. The Norsemen trimmed their beards, learned to drink wine instead of mead and ale, became Christians, built castles, and looked around for something to do next.

They never really lacked for something to do, for they were restless, energetic, troublesome fellows. They gave Europe some of its greatest leaders, as well as some of its greatest villains. Wherever

there was trouble—in those days, that was practically anywhere—there was almost sure to be a Norman in it. Chances were that he was in charge. Look up, in a history book or an encyclopedia, the story of Tancred of Hauteville and his sons, especially the one named Robert Guiscard, or Robert the Resourceful. Robert set himself up a kingdom in Sicily almost singlehanded. There was a fighter for you!

The Norse blood gave a needed lift to the descendants of Count Rolf. A century after his death, in the year 960, one of those descendants, a girl named Agnes, was carried off by a big redheaded

Viking named Arnulf Hairy-Arm. The pair lived long lives, and had eight children.

A hundred years later, their grandchildren and great-grandchildren still lived in Normandy. Some were knights or ladies, and one was a baron. Some were commoners. One of the commoners looked a good deal like his great-grandfather Arnulf. His name was Drogo, and he was big, redheaded, and strong, but he lacked the fiery temper to go with his red hair. He was easygoing and good-natured, without much ambition or much talent for pushing himself ahead.

Drogo was a common soldier, a man-at-arms in the castle guard of a minor Norman baron. He might have lived there contentedly all his life, and died there—except for certain events that took place in the summer of 1066.

Chapter 9:   The Knighting of Drogo the Red: A. D. 1066

Drogo the Red felt good, and when he felt good he sang, and when he sang he frightened all the rabbits and birds for a half-mile around. Rabbits and birds were about the only creatures there were to hear Drogo's tuneless bellows in the lonely forest he was riding through. There might be some outlaws about, but that didn't worry Drogo. Duke William of Normandy, a stern man, did a good job of keeping down outlaws. Besides, any bandit would be quite likely to flee in terror, thinking the frightful noise came from a troll or warlock rather than from a lone rider.

So Drogo rode happily along, with his feet out of the stirrups, beating his heels on the sides of the horse in time to the song, and sniffing the pleasant odors of a late summer day. The song was an old soldier's ballad about a faithful lady who had promised to keep a lamp lighted until her lord knight came home from the wars, and when he was killed the lamp went out, and the lady died of grief. It was a sad song, made sadder than ever by Drogo's unmelodious bass. But he liked it, and the patient old horse didn't seem to mind, and as for the rabbits and birds—why, they would just have to look out for themselves.

Drogo would have found it hard to explain why he was so joyous. It might have been because, for the first time in his twenty-four years, he was completely free. Three days before, he had left for all time the castle where he had been a man-at-arms. It was a gloomy place. Its lord was an evil-tempered tyrant, renowned for stinginess. Its lady was just as evil-tempered, and even stingier.

But Drogo had stayed on loyally, underpaid, underfed, and over-worked—until the baron unjustly accused him of stealing some wine; and the baroness hit him on the face for some clumsiness; and the chief of the castle guard said some nasty things about him in front of Drogo's own comrades. All of this, coming together, was just too much. Besides, it was high summer, everything was green, and the meadows around the castle gave off a tantalizing smell which almost overcame the sour stink of the moat.

Suddenly it had come to Drogo that he couldn't bear to stay in the dark, damp wooden castle one day longer.

He knew that Duke William of Normandy was gathering an army on the seacoast to conquer the island of England, of which he claimed to be the rightful king. Drogo knew little of England and cared less. But it sounded like an adventure. The baron had refused to have anything to do with this harebrained scheme of the Duke's and had warned his men against it, under threat of dire punishment. And that was enough for Drogo.

So three nights earlier he had gathered together his few belong-ings—the elderly horse, his arms and armor—and set out to join the Duke. One of the men-at-arms, a friend, let him out of the gate. Since then he had ridden steadily east by north. He had traveled through poor villages, past wooden castles on their earthen mounds and even one of the new stone ones, and through wall-encircled towns. He had talked with merchants, pilgrims, monks, soldiers, beggars, thieves. In general he had had a glorious time, and now two more days would bring him to the coast and William's army.

Further ahead than that, Drogo did not think. He was a good sol-dier, and he had a hunch it wouldn't be hard to find employment with one of the nobles or knights who were gathering under Wil-liam's banners. After all, he had a horse—not a very good one, but still a horse. He had a shabby hauberk and a casque of boiled leather;

he had a shield, a lance, and a good Norman sword, and what more did a soldier need?

So Drogo the Red rode on, singing ever more loudly, to the peril of rabbit and bird, the thirty-fourth verse of the old song:

"The lamp it burned with a fitful flare,
  And the fair dame watched it ever,
  Her eyes fixed on its burning glare
  For her lord who came back never.
  Oh, woe, sing wo-o-o-oe!
  For the lord who came back never!"

He broke off suddenly. Not far ahead another track merged with the one he was following, and through the trees he caught the flash of a red cloak. Shrugging his shield around into easier reach, he gripped his lance a bit tighter. It was a lonely spot, and bandits might think even his old horse was worth taking. He reined to a stop and watched warily.

Two men on horseback came out of the shadow of the trees, and Drogo relaxed. These were no bandits. One was a servant, but the other was obviously a knight. He was positively dazzling. Drogo whistled admiringly.

The knight was mounted on a glossy bay, big and beautiful. The horse, together with the arms and armor of the rider, would have cost nearly as much as the whole of the dingy castle Drogo had left behind. From the knight's shoulders hung a long red cloak embroidered in silver thread. His kite-shaped shield was red, with bronze bosses which sparkled in the sun. His lance—also red—he held stiffly erect.

But it was the knight's hauberk which made Drogo's eyes shine. It was new, shiny, like the rest of his outfit—a "great hauberk," reaching to his knees instead of just below the waist as Drogo's did. Furthermore, it was made of chain mail, iron rings cunningly fastened together. From under the elbow-length sleeves of his hauberk came the long red sleeves of his under-tunic, and the knight wore red stockings, cross-gartered in yellow leather. On his head sat a conical steel helmet with a nose guard, as new as all the rest, and at his side hung a long Norman sword in a painted scabbard worked in gold and **gems.**

Confronted with such magnificence, Drogo felt shabby. His own hauberk, iron rings sewed on leather, had saved his life more than once, but he felt distaste for it now. What would it be like to own such a beautiful piece of mail as the one the knight wore? The man who could afford it must be a very great lord indeed, in spite of the fact that he rode with only one servant. Drogo bowed respectfully and held up his arm, palm out, to show he had no hostile intention.

"Hail, Sir Knight!" he called.

The gorgeous rider did not even look his way, although the servant waved cheerfully and grinned. Drogo rode toward them, still smiling. As he came close he said, "I'm Drogo the Red, man-at-arms, on my way to join our good Duke. Do our paths run together?"

The knight said not a word, merely turned his horse and rode on slowly. He was very young, Drogo saw, not more than twenty-one, although the sour, arrogant, cold look on his thin face made him appear older.

A little damped by the chilly reception, Drogo reined in beside the servant. "What's the matter with him?" Drogo whispered. "Been drinking too much sour wine?"

The servant grinned again. He was a little older than his master, and resembled him not at all. Where the knight was tall and slender, the servant was short and stout. His chubby face was pleasant, but Drogo saw a glint of shrewdness in his blue eyes. The servant said nothing, only winked, and held back his horse to let the knight draw farther ahead of them.

When the red cloak was only a splash of color among the leaves, the servant said: "All right. We can talk now."

Drogo was puzzled. He had known many knights, good and bad, rich and poor. Some of them would sit all night and swap yarns with the men-at-arms. Others held themselves above lowly beings like common soldiers. But never had Drogo run across such a combination of pride and sourness as now. "Who is that young rooster, anyway?" he asked. "The Emperor's oldest son, or the King of the Moon Islands?"

The servant chuckled, and introduced himself as Tark. The knight, he said, was Sir Rollo de Vanz, second son of Baron Humphrey de Vanz, who held a sizable fief near the Flemish frontier. "Everyone calls him Rollo the Proud," Tark said, "although I think, myself, Rollo the Sour Face would be better."

In spite of his own dislike for the young knight, Drogo was a little shocked to hear the servant talk so. A knight's servant should be devoted to him. Drogo shrugged. It was none of his business.

"Is he like that all the time? I thought maybe he was under a vow of silence."

Tark shook his head. "The only vow he's under is one of conceit. Rollo's as sour as a boiled owl's head most of the time. The rest of the time he's angry. Unless, of course, he's trying to impress some high nobleman—then he smiles like a pig in a swill pail. Wait until you see him with Duke William."

"You're sailing with the Duke, then?"

"Rollo is going to let Duke William help him conquer England."

Drogo laughed. "That's nice of him. But how does it happen that you're the only one with him? With that outfit he's got on—"

"Fifteen of us started from Vanz," Tark said. "Rollo was so unbearable that one by one they deserted. Last night we had four others left besides me. This morning they'd all gone, Heaven knows where. Rollo hasn't said a word about it. I suppose he's too proud to take notice of such animals as men-at-arms. But he's been nastier than ever today." He sighed. "He'll probably take it out on me."

Drogo and Tark chatted amiably as their horses ambled on through the forest, out into a cleared space which had once been a village, and along a little stream. Rollo kept a hundred yards in front of them, never once turning his head.

The knight, Drogo learned, had been spoiled from the time he was a baby, by his father, his mother, and two maiden aunts. His older half-brother was a good enough sort of fellow, Tark said—not much brains, but plenty for his purposes. The half-brother, thirty years older than Rollo, would inherit old Baron Humphrey's lands, and in order to give Rollo what he considered a proper start in life, the old baron had sold a good many acres to buy the magnificent horse and armor. Rollo accepted them as only his just due. He had a tremendous notion of his own importance and an even more tremendous notion of the gulf which separated nobles from commoners.

"Why do you stick with him?" Drogo asked.

Tark shrugged. "What else can I do? I'm no soldier, no farmer, no artisan. I go where the wind blows me. Besides, I smell money in the wind that blows toward England."

The fat servant had a good sense of humor, and Drogo found himself laughing more and more often. Once or twice Rollo turned and glared evilly at them, but Drogo paid no attention. Then Tark said something especially funny, and Drogo guffawed.

The knight reined in, and as the other two came close he said coldly: "Stop that noise, you clods."

Drogo's laugh ended, but he shrugged cheerfully enough. He was not going to be insolent, although the cold contempt in the young knight's voice lighted a little flame of anger inside him. Never had he known such an ill-tempered puppy! The day was too fine for him to stay angry long, though, and in a little while he and Tark were talking companionably again. Then something reminded Drogo of a song he hadn't thought of in years. Tark thought he knew it, but wasn't sure, so Drogo started to sing it for him.

Before he had got out more than three words, Sir Rollo turned the bay horse and spurred back to them, his face dark with anger. "I told you to be quiet," he said harshly. "I don't give orders more than once, clown."

The flame of anger sprang up inside Drogo again. "Look, Sir Rollo," he said carefully, "this is a fine day, made for singing. We're hurting no one. I'll stop if it offends you, but there's no need—"

The knight was not listening. "Get back out of sight. I'll not have you near me."

The anger burned brighter. "Sir Knight," Drogo said, "I respect your rank, but you're not my master, nor am I your man. It's not—"

"Tark," Sir Rollo snapped, "see that this fellow keeps back. If I have no companions of noble birth, at least I can be spared the grunting of hogs."

This was something new. Not the proudest knight of Drogo's acquaintance would have spoken so to a man-at-arms. Rollo was a knight and Drogo only a common soldier. But he was a man, and a fighting man at that.

"Hog! I'm no hog, young sir! Best remember it takes more than a new hauberk to make a knight. We're not on your land. I'll laugh when I please and sing when I please and ride where I please, and if your lordship doesn't like it, he can go someplace else!"

"So the cur snaps, does it?" said Sir Rollo in a tone of icy contempt. Then he turned and trotted off until he had put about twenty yards between them.

Tark looked anxious. "Watch him," he murmured. "I don't like the way he's acting."

Suddenly Rollo wheeled his horse and came thundering straight at Drogo. His mouth was twisted in a snarl, and vicious hate gleamed in his eyes.

Why, he's mad! Drogo thought.

The knight held his eight-foot lance poised in the old style, over his shoulder, ready to deliver a blow. "Insolence from a dog!" he cried, as the horse galloped at Drogo. "The dog must learn its lesson!"

"No, Sir Rollo!" Tark shouted. He tried to spur between the two, but Drogo shoved him aside.

With the instinct of a soldier he reacted quickly to the sudden attack. His shield came forward to guard his vulnerable left side, and his lance swung down. At the same time he dug in his spurs, and the old horse jumped forward.

But Drogo held his lance in the new way—hugged under his arm next to his body, a style of lance-fighting just beginning to come into use. Held that way—couched—the lance could not be moved so freely but it dealt a far heavier blow, with the solid weight of the rider's body behind it.

There was no time to think. The knight was almost upon him. Drogo forgot everything but the point of the lance aimed at his vitals. Rollo might be a belted knight, but Drogo, the common soldier, was a veteran of many a hard-fought battle. He was a professional.

The knight still held his lance high as if he meant to hurl it. As the horses came together, Rollo half-rose in his stirrups and drove the weapon forward at Drogo's face. Drogo swayed a little to the right. The point of the knight's lance scraped harmlessly across his shield.

But Drogo's point slammed into Rollo's red shield exactly where he had aimed, just to the left of the center boss. The shock of contact pushed Drogo back in his saddle and made the old horse stumble, but he clamped his fingers tighter around the lance shaft and shoved with all his strength.

Rollo's breath left his body with a grunt. His legs flew up, and turning a half-somersault backward, he sailed into the air, then landed on his shoulders on the soft ground. Lance and shield flew wide.

Drogo reined in, laughing. He had no wish to hurt the knight, nasty as the young fellow was; he only wanted to teach him a lesson. As he turned his horse, he saw that Tark had dismounted and was running toward his master. Drogo, too, dismounted, laid down shield and lance, and walked toward the fallen knight. Tark was helping Rollo to his feet. The knight stood uncertainly for a second or two; then, with a shriek of rage, he swung his fist and caught the fat servant under the chin. Tark stumbled backward and sat down.

"What did you do that for?" Drogo asked. "The poor fellow was only trying to help you." He bent over Tark to pick him up.

114

The servant's eyes widened. "Look out!" he cried shrilly. "Behind—"

Instinctively Drogo fell to one knee. There was a vicious "swish" as a heavy blow knocked his leather casque from his head. Half-stunned, he rolled over on the ground to escape the second blow he knew would come.

Rollo, lips drawn back, was running at him with drawn sword. "Filth!" he snarled. "Dog!" The sword flashed in a wide sweep, but Drogo scrambled out of the way, crouching low. He fumbled for his own sword. The knight's blade caught the front of his hauberk. Its heavy metal rings stopped the blow, but a wave of pain swept through him. Luckily the blow slowed Rollo enough so that Drogo had time to draw his own sword and catch Rollo's next sweep on its hilt.

It was kill or be killed, Drogo knew. Rollo was mad with hate. Drogo knew the dire penalty for slaying a knight, but there was no time to worry about that. Their swords clanged together as Rollo thrust again. Tark knelt, frozen, watching with open mouth.

Drogo fell back warily, protecting himself as best he could. There was little swordsmanship in Rollo's wild attack. His blade made flashing circles in the air as he tried to close in, muttering, "I'll kill ...kill...dog..."

Never had Drogo met a man who could swing a sword so fast. One blow followed another, and he could barely manage to fend them off. Each time the jar against his own blade almost numbed his arm. Rollo showed no sign of weakening or slowing down. His cuts rained ever faster—left, right, down—as the blades ground together with a metallic whine.

Drogo breathed a prayer. Rollo was surely mad! This could not go on! He stumbled over a half-buried root and twisted to dodge a blow that would have beheaded him. He felt the beginning of panic in his belly.

Then his eyes narrowed. "I can get him," Drogo thought. There was no craft in the knight's attack, nothing but blind fury. Another blow came whistling at Drogo's head. Instead of parrying it with his blade, he ducked under. Rollo's sword cut into the earth and the knight swayed, off balance for a second.

The second was all that Drogo needed.

With a quick jerk, he brought his blade up over Rollo's in a backhand cut. The heavy sword caught Rollo under the chin, in one of the few places not protected by the metal links. There was a dull, wet sound.

Rollo stood quite still. The madness faded from his eyes, and a look of utter surprise took its place. He made a small movement with his sword. A torrent of blood was gushing from the wound.

Then there was nothing in his eyes, nothing at all. Slowly his knees buckled under him, and he fell face down.

Drogo leaned on his sword, breathing heavily. Horror was beginning to creep over him. He had killed men in battle, but never had he met anything like the frenzy of Rollo. "He was mad," Drogo said hoarsely. "I had to kill him. You see that, don't you? He was mad. I had to…"

Tark got to his feet slowly, staring at Rollo's body, and walked over jerkily to stand beside his fallen master. "Yes, I suppose he was mad. Mad with arrogance and conceit and hatred." He gave a short laugh. "So ends the brief career of Sir Rollo of Vanz, called the Proud. He dreamed of glory, of honor, of fame. He dies alone in a boggy forest, attended by one fat servant, killed by a common soldier. He was just twenty-one years old—knighted a month ago, on his birthday."

Drogo felt a queer sickness. There was no triumph in this victory, only a dull distaste and a wish to be elsewhere. One month a knight! He fell on his knees and tried to think of a prayer for Rollo. In a few minutes he felt Tark's hand on his shoulder.

"Don't take it so hard. Rollo was only a bad-tempered, foolish boy playing at being a knight. You did what you had to do. But, my red-haired friend, that won't help you if you're found here with his body."

"I'll bury him in the woods," Drogo said dully. He got to his feet, wiped his sword on the grass, and sheathed it. "You get out of this, Tark. Once I'm with William's army, no one will bother me."

Tark shook his head. "Oh, no, Master Drogo. Do you think I can face old Sir Humphrey and try to explain how his favorite son came to be killed by a wandering soldier? Or should I try to make my way alone? No, thank you. I have a better idea."

"What is it?"

Tark pointed to Rollo's body. "No one in this part of the country knows Sir Rollo of Vanz, or knows he was going to join William. Outside of his own family, nobody knows where he is supposed to be. It will be months before the old baron even begins to think he should be hearing from him. Meanwhile—"

"Meanwhile, you and I are with William in England, a couple of men-at-arms. Good!"

Tark smiled. "You *are* slow. More than that, friend Drogo." He pointed to the handsome bay horse, grazing calmly a few steps away. "Do we leave him to the wolves? Foolishness! We join William's army, all right—but not as men-at-arms. You will ride in proudly, a knight from some far-off district. I'm your faithful squire."

"You're crazy!" Drogo shouted. "You're as crazy as he was!"

"Am I? Who will question you if you tell them you're Sir Whozis of Wherever? Knights from all over Christendom are joining William. You ride Rollo's horse, wear his gear, and you're as good as any of them."

Drogo turned violently away. "I'm no knight! I'm only a common soldier! You heard what he called me—dog!" Drogo knew that Rollo had been an uncommonly nasty young man, but he had also been a knight, initiated into that almost mystic bond of knighthood. And Drogo had a great reverence for knighthood. "It's not right—"

"You big blockhead!" Tark was growing angry. "We stand here arguing, and at any minute someone's likely to come along. Where are we then, eh? You balk because you're not a knight? Well, I'll fix that right now!" He drew back his fist. "I dub thee knight, Sir Drogo the Red!" His fist slammed into Drogo's shoulder, and Drogo staggered under the blow. Tark might be fat, but he was husky. "Now will you hurry and get that body hidden, and climb into Rollo's armor?"

Drogo still protested feebly. He'd be recognized and exposed. Rollo's horse or weapons would be recognized. The marshals in William's army would know all the knightly families. Besides, it wasn't right—

Tark was hopping from one foot to another. "I haven't been a servant to Baron Humphrey for nothing. I'll fix up a pedigree for you that will convince anybody. There's a small chance somebody will spot you, but isn't it worth taking a chance, to see your sons barons in England, Sir Drogo?"

That did it. *Sir* Drogo. It had a certain ring. He tried it aloud. "Sir Drogo." After all, he had been with knights enough to be able to imitate their manners—some of them had no more manners than a bull, anyhow. And to have his sons barons in England—

"I think I hear somebody coming!" Tark pleaded in an agonized voice. "It's Sir Drogo now, but it's Sir Hangman's Meat if we're found with this body! Hurry!" He grabbed Rollo's feet and began to drag the body into the trees. Drogo wavered for a second, then lifted the slain knight's shoulders.

An hour later, Sir Drogo the Red, in a hauberk which had been cleaned of its bloodstains, rode out of the forest on a handsome bay. Behind him rode his squire, leading an old horse which plodded along patiently, bearing some spare gear. The body of Sir Rollo was buried and the grave covered with rocks and brush; it would be a long time before anyone found it.

Drogo felt a little uncomfortable in his inherited finery, but already his depression was beginning to pass. Death was too common a thing for it to bother him overmuch. And, as Tark had said, Rollo was no great loss. Tark had convinced him, also, that the possibility of discovery was slight. He would use some of Rollo's money to buy a new tunic and cloak on the remote chance that someone might recognize Rollo's and ask embarrassing questions. They would sell the horse, too, or trade it. In the hubbub and turmoil of an invasion of England, it was hardly likely there would be any hue and cry after an unknown young knight from a distant spot.

All in all, matters could have been much worse. It felt strange, though—masquerading as a knight. But what was a knight but a soldier, and what was Drogo but a soldier—a better one than poor mad Rollo? The gorgeous mail hauberk sat comfortably on his wide shoulders; the fine stuff of the tunic was soft to the touch; the powerful shoulders of the bay moved easily under the saddle.

They passed some peddlers leading pack mules, and the peddlers greeted them with deference. Drogo sat straighter in the saddle and nodded to them.

Sir Drogo. Sons who would be barons in England.

Shadows began to lengthen. The grave under the rocks, the fight under the trees, seemed farther away with each step the bay took. In a few days he would be with Duke William—a knight.

They overtook a party of merchants and monks hurrying toward the next town, fearful of being benighted in the forest. The merchants pulled their animals from the road and bowed obsequiously. One asked, in a timid voice: "Sir knight, we beg your protection on this lonely road. There are robbers—"

Drogo nodded curtly. "You may ride with us." He spoke over his shoulder to Tark, and there was a new ring of authority in his

120

voice. "Let these good people stay with us, squire. But they must mend their pace. We have a long road to travel."

Tark ducked his head, hiding a delighted grin. "Yes, gentle sir," he said humbly. "Yes, Sir Drogo."

Chapter 10: The Training of a Knight

Nobody ever found out about Sir Rollo, so far as Drogo knew. This was not surprising. The population was sparse, and communication slow and infrequent. Doubtless Rollo's people thought he had decided not to return home directly, and there was certainly no lack of ways by which a man could get himself killed. Perhaps they thought he had died in the great battle at Hastings in which Duke William won the crown of England.

Drogo's conscience didn't bother him much, at least not to the point where he couldn't bear it. He was much more concerned over his masquerade as a knight than over his killing of Sir Rollo. But long before the battle at Hastings, on October 14, 1066, his faint pangs had worn off.

He fought with the other Norman knights in this battle that broke the power of the Saxons. Harold, the last Saxon king of England, died with an arrow in his eye, and William became king. During the battle, Drogo happened to be close to William when the duke was attacked by three huge Saxon "housecarls," members of the Saxon king's bodyguard. Drogo beat them off singlehanded, and William got the idea that Drogo had saved his life.

After he became King William I, and everybody called him "The Conqueror," he rewarded Drogo with a fine manor house and wide lands in Kent, south of London. The house and lands had belonged to a Saxon noble who had fallen at Harold's side.

Unlike many of the Norman lords, Drogo did not throw the Saxons out. He took the name of de Wyke, from the manor, which was called Wykeford. He even married a daughter of the family, and for the rest of his days lived more or less peacefully on his rich acres. He died in 1101, a wealthy and respected man. Tark lived on, beyond the age of ninety, an unheard-of thing in those days. Before he died his mind wandered, and he muttered crazy things about a fight in the forest and a knight named Rollo, but nobody paid any attention. Old Tark was cherished as a relic of the Conquest. The father of that Sir Roger de Wyke who fought in the Holy Land remembered the old squire.

Drogo's son William—named after the duke—and his grandson Nicholas never dreamed that the man who had saved the Conqueror's life at Hastings had been a mere commoner, base born. It was just as well they didn't know, for it would have bothered them considerably. By that time the notion that people of gentle birth were somehow different from commoners was firmly fixed. Everyone believed that a gentleman could easily be distinguished from a base born man, even if both were stripped naked.

And actually there was some truth in this idea. The gentlefolk ate better and lived better, and didn't wear themselves out slaving all their lives on a starvation diet. They grew taller, and in general were healthier, than the serfs or laborers. The gentles weren't tied to the handle of a plough from sunup to sundown, nor so weary at night they could think of nothing but sleep. They had time for pleasure and sport. They liked to fight, but if there was no fighting going on, they hunted or went hawking or held tournaments. They had time for what we call culture today—music, poetry, art, philosophy. Most of it was pretty primitive by our standards, but it was a lot better than nothing at all.

The feudal system was solidly set, and people accepted it as the natural order of things. At the top was the king, who owed fealty only to God. Below the king were his barons-in-chief. Below them were the descending ranks of nobles and gentlefolk, and below them the descending ranks of commoners. At the very bottom were the serfs—laborers, peasants, humble folk who were regarded as not much better than animals. Even among serfs there were gradations, down to the miserable creatures who were slaves and had no more rights than so many hogs. But at least these lowly people *belonged* somewhere, and poor as they were, they despised those who had no place at all—the outlaws, the "masterless men," the wandering jugglers and players, who were considered outcasts. No matter how lowly a serf might be, he had a place in society, a place where he was accepted. It was a comfortable feeling. Very few ever bettered their station in life, except through the Church; but on the other hand, very few ever lost it, unless they broke the law, or became afflicted with leprosy—in which case they were regarded as dead.

Gentlefolk had considerable free time, and what to do with it became a problem. Over the years they worked up a code of manners and customs, things to do and things not to do. Part of this elaborate code was apparently designed merely to provide them with ways of keeping busy (long winters in those chilly stone castles must have been fearfully boring). Some of the social customs were simply a means of showing that they, the gentlefolk, were different from common people, who did not know the correct way to behave.

For example, it was extremely important to know the right method of carving each kind of meat at the table, and boys spent years learning the art. If a squire botched the job, he was disgraced. In the same way, the gentles invented a whole new language having to do with hunting, a sport followed with passionate enthusiasm by every gentleman and most gentlewomen. If you talked about seeing a herd of pigs, for instance, you marked yourself as a low-grade boor unfit to associate with gentlemen. You had to say "a sounder of swine."

Every kind of bird had to be referred to differently. To be correct, you had to say a wisp of snipe, a badling of ducks, a fall of woodcock, a nye of pheasants. Nobody but a thick-head or a fool would talk about a nye of woodcock or a badling of pheasants.

Gentlefolk had to learn many trivial things like these, things which set them apart from commoners. All these things had to be studied, and there were so many of them! If a boy wanted to be a knight—and what boy didn't?—he had to begin at the age of seven or thereabouts. Usually he was taken from his home and sent to school at the castle of one of the great barons, perhaps that of his father's feudal overlord. At first he was given over to the women, whose job it was to make human beings out of little savages. The ladies of the castle taught them to eat without gobbling their food like wolves (the table manners of the ladies would turn us pale, but at least they followed certain rules) and how to behave in the house.

These little fellows were called pages, and as they grew older they had an increasing list of duties to perform. They waited on the ladies. They ran errands. They began to learn the endless list of terms applied to hunting, to falconry, to serving at table. They might be taught to read and write by a priest, who also taught them religion. And always, they had the idea drilled into them that some day they would be knights.

When the boys could sneak away from their duties, they loved to loiter about the stables or the armory, caring for the horses, or listening wide-eyed to the older boys—the esquires or squires, apprentice knights. When the pages reached the age of fourteen, they could hope to pass over to this high estate themselves. From the time a boy graduated from pagehood until he won his golden spurs, he was an esquire, and spent most of his time practicing with weapons. Esquire means "shield-bearer," and when he grew older—sixteen or so—that's exactly what he was. He was assigned to the personal service of his lord, or of some other knight. He carried the knight's heavy shield for him on journeys. He attended to the knight, armed him for tournament or battle, kept his weapons in good condition, got him out of danger if he were wounded. And all the time, of course, he was supposed to be learning the principles of chivalry from his master—courage, honor, faith, devotion to duty—and the **use of arms.**

Esquires also had to learn how to sing, to dance, to play a musical instrument, and to compose songs and poems. Probably most of them considered these studies a horrible waste of time. They were supposed to learn how to behave with women, too: to treat them with gentleness and courtesy, to protect them, and to make love to them with ease and skill. Undoubtedly they enjoyed these lessons.

On the whole, though, the esquire had a rugged life. He spent hour after hour in the practice yard under the stern eye of an old professional, learning how to handle weapons. He swung a heavy, blunt sword at a post, or staged mock fights with other esquires. Hour after hour in the saddle, learning how to manage a horse with one hand and his knees, or with no hands at all. Hour after hour in heavy armor until he became so accustomed to it that he was scarcely aware of having it on. Sometimes he wore the armor for days without taking it off.

He learned to shrug off bruises and cuts which would send a modern boy to the hospital. Wounds, after all, would be commonplace in his life. The squire-master might order him to go for a day, or two days, without food, just to get him used to the idea of going hungry. He might have to spend a whole winter night running up and down the castle yard; or sleep without blankets in a driving rain; or carry a hundred-pound pack on his back from dawn to dusk. All this was intended to toughen him up. It did, too.

Night after night, year after year, a squire would drag himself from the tilting yard dog-tired, aching, bruised, hungry. And next day he had nothing to look forward to but more of the same. A hard life, indeed. But if the squire stuck out the course of training until he reached manhood, he discovered it had been worthwhile. He grew up strong and tough, able to laugh at a wound or a bruise. He could handle lance or sword with the easy skill of a professional, standing in the hot sun for hours swinging an ax and never breathe hard. He was ready for his life's work—fighting.

Some, of course, did not stick it through. The weak ones decided that military life was not for them, and got out, probably to enter holy orders. And of course a good many simply did not survive. A wound, or a broken bone, or those nights in the rain, killed them off. Too bad, of course, but it was best to find out if they were made of the proper stuff. And there were always others to take their places.

To many boys of gentle blood, a career of fighting had no appeal at all. Most of these went into the Church, to become monks or priests. That was really about the only choice they had, except to become a kind of hanger-on, scorned by women and men alike. A very few, more determined or more clever than the rest, might find

128

some career outside the Church which would exempt them from fighting yet still be respectable. For the great majority, however, there was nothing else, nothing at all.

Many squires never became knights. They lived out their lives in service to wealthier or more able men who had won their golden spurs, or they became part of the household of a lord. It cost a good deal to be knighted, and many a boy without money stayed a simple squire, eating his heart out because some friend had become a lordly knight. Others just didn't care. There were many responsibilities that went with knighthood, and they preferred not to accept them. They chose to stay squires, just as today some sergeants in the army, offered commissions as officers, choose to stay in the ranks.

But if the squire was finally judged worthy and admitted into knighthood—ah, there was a proud young man! Remember that nobody ever was *born* a knight, no matter how exalted his family. He might be born a baron or an earl or even a king, but he achieved knighthood on his own merits. (Some unworthy ones sneaked in the back door, to be sure. Powerful, wealthy fathers might see to it that their sons were granted golden spurs even though they didn't know a lance from a turning-spit, or were stupid to the point of idiocy, or laughed at the knightly ideals of chivalry. But these cases were comparatively rare, and even such candidates had to go through a form of training and acceptance.)

There was almost always a ceremony connected with the "adubment," the making of a knight. The ceremony varied widely from country to country and from century to century. It might be a simple, hurried phrase spoken on a battlefield, or a week-long festivity with feasting and pageantry. High point of the ceremony was usually the words, "I dub thee knight," accompanied by a tap on the candidate's shoulder with a fist or the flat of a sword. The tap varied from a gentle touch to a lusty knock that sometimes sent the candidate sprawling.

Gradually, more and more elements were added to the ceremony. At its best, the knighting of a young man was an occasion of both joy and solemnity, of deep spiritual significance. The candidate was dressed in white, to signify purity. He held a night-long vigil over his arms, which rested before an altar, while he prayed for strength,

courage, and steadfastness. He was bathed and clothed in festive garments while his sponsors, older knights, spoke of the duties and responsibilities of knighthood.

Finally, before a glittering company assembled in the Great Hall of the castle, the candidate came forth. His sword was girded on, usually with some admonition like, "Draw this only in defense of the right, in protection of the weak, in redress of wrong." His golden spurs were buckled on, and at last, as he knelt humbly, the king or a great nobleman dealt him the blow on the shoulder which admitted him to knighthood.

Then the feasting began, with the new knight, of course, the center of attention. Everybody congratulated him, wished him well, foretold great feats of daring and bravery. Pretty girls hung on his arm, and everybody flattered him with attention.

Then all the long, arduous, tedious years were forgotten. He was a man—and a knight.

For the sixteenth time that afternoon, young Nicholas de Wyke kicked the patient horse and lowered his blunt lance. The old beast started forward at a lumbering trot, gradually gathering a little speed.

Nick hardly saw the wooden shield of the quintain. His head ached and his eyes blurred. His right arm and shoulder felt as if they would drop off at any minute, and shafts of pure agony ran up and down his back. He tried to focus his eyes on the quintain, where a battered board was nailed to one arm of a horizontal pivot on a post. From the other arm of the pivot hung a bag of sand. The trick was to strike the board squarely with the lance, then ride on, out of the way, before the sandbag came around and slammed you in the back.

Nick knew he would do it all wrong.

He didn't mind the aches. He generally ached somewhere, and he was used to it. What caused the lump in his stomach and the sour taste in his throat was the conviction that he would botch the job. He always did.

Faintly, Nick heard the hoarse voice of old Thomas, the tiltyard master, shouting at him: "Mind your point! Hold steady!" Mixed with Thomas' advice came the jeering cries of the other five squires, who had run the course successfully.

He blinked and tried to recall all the things he was supposed to do. Left arm out from body, reins chest-high, feet braced, buttocks firm against the cantle of the saddle, knees gripping firmly, weight balanced, body firm but not rigid, lance under armpit, gripped in the hand, not the fingers—and, finally, he must be ready to take the shock with his whole body . . .

He couldn't concentrate at all. Let me hit it squarely, let the sand-bag miss me! he thought muddily. Please, let me do it right so that they won't laugh! If I do, Thomas will let me quit for today. If the afternoon would only end; if I could get a sup of ale, and bread, and maybe a bit of bacon, and crawl into bed!

The horse galloped on, taking not the slightest interest. It had been carrying squires in the tiltyard for too many years to have any feelings about the matter.

The quintain board bobbed up and down before Nick. Frantic, trying to remember everything at once, he saw at the last minute that his point was far too low. He made a desperate effort to raise it, but the heavy practice lance felt like lead. Completely missing the board with his point, he hit it with his elbow. The pivot creaked, and the sandbag flew around and whacked him heavily in the back.

Nick fought to keep his saddle as the old horse slowed its clumsy gallop, turned, and walked back toward Thomas. When the animal stopped, Nick slid from its back and stood swaying.

"Didn't even hit the shield!" Thomas shook his grizzled head. "Young sir, you learn nothing! Nothing! I've told you a hundred times, the lance is only a stick of wood without a clever arm to guide it."

The dull rebellion which had been seething inside Nick bubbled to the surface. "Oh, let me alone!" he cried.

Thomas looked at him with mingled exasperation and pity, and took the reins. " 'Twill do no good to try more today. Maybe tomorrow—" His tone held grave doubt that tomorrow would bring any improvement. "Get along, Nick."

The other squires came sauntering over, their faces alight with wicked glee. "Sir Lancelot returned to life!" said Hal Boutelier, better known as Sparrow.

134

Nick said nothing, but threw Sparrow a look of hatred. Sparrow came only to Nick's shoulder, but when they met in mock combat, it was always big, slow Nick who was beaten. Sparrow was eighteen, six months older than Nick, and he took great delight in teasing the larger but younger boy. Nick walked ahead of the others toward squires' hall, the bare, barn-like room where they lived, trying to keep his aches from being too obvious.

Sparrow followed, one hand on the shoulder of John of Denby, and the others trooped after. "Mark his swagger!" Sparrow said in a tone of mock wonder. "Truly, John, we are watching the marvel of the age. He doesn't hit the quintain with his lance, as we common folk must do. Not Lancelot de Wyke! He does it with his elbow! Oh, we can learn much from this hero. How not to sit a saddle—there's one lesson from our Nick. How not to hold a shield. If you want to handle a lance like a serf with a forkful of hay, watch Nick."

"Oh, quit it, Sparrow," said good-natured John. "He's bruised and tired."

"Tired? Our Nick? Why, he's a very ox in armor!"

It was too much. With a wordless roar, Nick turned and hurled himself at Sparrow. His wildly flailing fist caught Sparrow a glancing blow on the side of the head. Clumsy as it was, there was strength behind it, and Sparrow, his laugh gone, sat down suddenly in the tiltyard mud. Nick threw himself on his tormentor. Sparrow wriggled furiously, pounding Nick's face, but Nick held him down and began to plaster mud in his hair. John of Denby tried vainly to pull them apart.

"Stop that! Stop, I say!" The harsh bellow penetrated even Nick's anger. Half-hysterical though he was, he knew better than to disobey Sir Bellamy, the fierce knight who had charge of squires and pages. "Stand up!"

Nick rolled to his feet and stood panting. "For shame, Hal Boutelier! And you, Nicholas de Wyke! Who started this brawl?"

"I did, sir." As usual, Sparrow spoke first. It was a knight's part to accept blame. "I goaded Nick."

"No! It was I who—"

"Be silent!" Sir Bellamy snapped. With a helpless feeling, Nick looked at the horribly scarred face of the knight. He seemed to be snarling, but that was the fault of the scar which twisted his features and drew his mouth back in a perpetual grimace. "Go to squires' hall, Boutelier, and clean yourself. And you, John, and the rest of you. You stay here, Nicholas."

The others went through the gate in the curtain-wall, into the inner keep. Sir Bellamy turned to Nick. "Walk with me and cool off." Nick, still simmering, fell into step beside the squire-master and they began a slow pacing down the tiltyard.

"Thomas tells me," the knight said, "that you tried the quintain sixteen times today and made a fair hit not once."

"Thomas tells the truth," Nick said sullenly.

Sir Bellamy glanced at Nick. The knight was a big man, but their heads were on a level. "What ails you, son? You're not stupid. There is strength in your arm—you're stronger than many men grown. Yet you don't improve at all with lance or sword. Last week I watched you at the hacking post." He shook his head. "Your strokes were slow and clumsy, and once you even dropped the sword. What's the matter?"

Nick shrugged, and a feeling of hopelessness welled up inside him. "I don't know. In my mind I hit the quintain every course." He tapped his forehead. "I have everything up here. I know how to disarm Sparrow, as clever as he is with a sword. Yet when we meet under the eyes of Thomas and the others, he beats me every time. And they all laugh."

"Ah?" said Sir Bellamy, interested. "And how would you disarm young Spar——young Boutelier?"

Nick answered eagerly. "He presses always, circling to his right. I have marked it many times. Instead of circling with him, I would fall back a pace very quickly, step to the left, and be inside his guard. Then—"

"So, so." The knight nodded in satisfaction. "And that is what I would do, too. Why don't you do it, then?"

"I don't know. I think of it, and then I think I might do it wrong and they would laugh, and the chance is gone."

"And what do you think of when you're riding at the quintain?"

"Of all the things that Thomas has taught us. Keeping my eyes on the target, and not leaning too far forward or back, and—"

"And clamping the lance firmly and not letting the reins slack. I know. And do you also think of doing it wrong and having the others laugh at you?"

"Yes, sir," admitted Nick miserably.

They walked on a few steps. When Sir Bellamy spoke again, his voice was almost gentle. "Do you know, Nick, how old I was when I won knighthood? I was forty-four years old. And the deed that won my golden spurs also won me this." He touched his ruined face. "Forty-four, Nick. Yet I was of as good blood as others. My father was a brave man, but poor and luckless. I never had money to pay for my adubment. I had no sponsor. And until more than half my life was over, I never had the chance to perform a feat of arms which would bring me knighthood."

Nick felt he should say something, but could not think what to say.

"I saw other squires being girded knights, and my heart nearly broke. Till long after my youth was gone I was a squire, serving men no better than I was. No, by St. Peter! Not as good." He stopped and faced Nick. "You don't have that to face, Nick. In two or three years you will be knighted. Your father has a heavy purse. You'll not know the heart-sickness I did. But, my boy, you may know a worse one. Can you take the oath of knighthood, knowing that little pages laugh at you when you handle a sword? Can you take part in a tourney when you can't even hit the quintain? What will you do in battle, when your life may depend on your skill?"

Big as he was, Nick was close to tears. "What's the matter with me, Sir Bellamy?"

"Your trouble is not in strength or skill, Nick. Your trouble is in your mind and spirit."

"I'm no coward, sir!" Nick said indignantly.

"Aren't you?" Sir Bellamy asked softly. He raised his hand. "Oh, I don't mean you're frightened of being hurt or even killed. You'll fight bravely enough when the time comes, I have no doubt. But you'll lose. Why? Because you'll beat yourself. You're afraid you'll be laughed at. You're thinking all the time of yourself. You're so afraid of doing something wrong that you tell yourself you *will* do it wrong. So you do. D'you see?"

"Ye-es," Nick said doubtfully.

"You worry too much. Riding at the quintain, for example: your knees, your seat, your hands. You think of them all separately, so you never do anything right." Sir Bellamy frowned, trying to find words to express what he wanted to say. "You ought to run a course at the quintain as easily and unthinkingly"—he pointed toward the dovecote—"as that bird settles itself on its perch."

Some boys of ten or eleven, pages in the livery of Baron Odesham, were hopping around at one side of the tiltyard, fencing with wooden swords. One of them seemed to be pretending to be a bear. Two others were running around him, shouting with laughter and slapping him on the backside with their mock swords. "Nick, Nick, slow as a stick!" they shrieked.

Nick flushed painfully. Little devils! The pages were forever sneaking into squires' hall and putting dead fish from the moat into his bed, or filling his boots with boiled mush.

"Begone, you young rascals!" Sir Bellamy roared, and the youngsters scampered away, still laughing.

Nick knotted his fists. "I hate them! I hate the tiltyard and the armor and Thomas and everything here! I'll never be a knight!"

"You will certainly never be a knight if you think that way!" Sir Bellamy said sternly. "There is more to being a knight than skill with arms, Nick. There is a strength of mind, a calmness, a self-confidence that Thomas can't teach you, or I, or anyone else. But you have to learn it." He gave Nick a push on the shoulder. "Get you to the chapel to pray, and ask Sir Jerome to pray with you."

Miserably, Nick walked off, through the inner keep and into the castle itself. None of the soldiers or servants paid him the slightest attention. He glanced into the Great Hall, where trestle-boards were being set up for the evening meal, and finally came to the chilly little chapel.

Nick prayed for an hour, and the prayers helped him to compose himself. Gentle old Sir Jerome—the "Sir" was a title of honor given priests—found him there, listened to his story, and preached him a homily. The priest's impromptu sermon had to do with duty to family, the honor of knighthood, an account of Sir Jerome's pilgrimage to the Holy Land, a description of the ancient ruins of Rome, and observations on the habits of the badger. Everyone loved Sir Jerome, but his sermons were more likely to bewilder than inspire.

"Will I ever be a good knight, Sir Jerome?" Nick asked mournfully.

"And what else would you be, son? A priest? A monk?"

The boy shook his head. A religious life held no appeal for him. He was no scholar. He knew no craft, he knew nothing about trade, and even if he had, it was unthinkable that the eldest son of Sir William de Wyke should be anything but a knight.

He thought of the boys he knew back home at Wykeford. Many a summer's day he had spent with Tom o' the Mill and Dick, Andrew's son, not at all bothered by difference in rank. But on his last visit home, he found they had grown apart. Tom was learning his father's craft, happy at the prospect of spending his life in the clacking, dusty mill. Dick was already a farmer like his father, and was talking of marrying plump, pretty Meg Burle. He envied them. They knew what their lives were going to be. But he, Nick de Wyke, son of a famed knight—what was to become of him? What use was a knight who stumbled over his own feet, who couldn't run a course at a quintain? He asked Sir Jerome.

"God can help you, if He will," said the priest thoughtfully. "But I have noticed that He usually asks a firm foundation to build on. Sir Bellamy may well be right—you think too much of yourself. Try thinking about other people. That is the vow a knight takes, after all. And if you believe you can be a good knight, Nicholas, God will help you to be one."

The talk comforted Nick, and he made peace with Sparrow before they went to bed. For once the pages had not been up to their tricks, either; they hadn't even unlaced the thongs of his bedframe. In the morning Nick awoke with a high resolve to show everyone that he was as good a fighting man as the best. "Confidence!" he told himself. "That's the answer. Tell myself I'm going to hit the quintain, and I will!"

There was considerable excitement building up at Odesham. Little Ralph, the baron's youngest son, was going away to become a page at the great castle of the Earl of Murrey, in spite of his invalid mother's tearful protests. Ralph was a lively youngster, full of devilment and a favorite in squires' hall. As the squires breakfasted, Ralph came running in and announced gleefully that he had persuaded his father to allow the six squires to form part of his escort.

"Mama's sick, and my father can't go," the boy said, hopping from one foot to the other. "And we have to go through the Great Forest! And Alwain the Wolf's in there! And all his outlaws, and robbers!"

The squires greeted the news with cheers. Murrey Castle was about fifty miles from Odesham, and with proper management the trip meant at least a week away from Thomas and the tiltyard. Travel, adventure, vacation—and rumor said there were a good many pretty girls at Murrey. Maybe even some danger, although the squires had scant hope of that. There were certainly outlaws aplenty in the Great Forest. Alwain the Wolf was highly successful at robbing merchants and peddlers, but there was no record of his ever having attacked a band of armed men.

Still, the trip meant a holiday, and the squires tossed little Ralph from one to another, while the boy squealed happily.

Baron Odesham himself came to the tiltyard that morning to watch the squires go through their paces. Even pale, ill Lady Jehanne was carried down from her bower and lay on a bed in the tiltyard to watch. The whole household, in fact, turned out—knights of the meinie, men-at-arms, ladies, servants, and the little imps of pages.

Nick was not overjoyed at this, but he kept repeating to himself: "Confidence! I can do as well as Sparrow and John today. Better. Everyone will be watching me and cheering. I've got confidence."

The squires made their bows before the baron and his lady. The first thing Nick did was to get his feet tangled in a sword and fall flat on his face before them. They pretended not to notice, although even Lady Jehanne's wasted face showed the ghost of a smile, and one of the knights said with a laugh, "Now there's a trick with the sword I've never seen before!"

That was only the beginning. In a bout with John of Denby, using blunted swords, Nick was so hopelessly inept that Thomas stopped them from sheer embarrassment. Desperately, Nick muttered, "Confidence!" to combat the dull despair which was creeping through him. "I'll do better at the quintain," he told himself, trying to stifle a voice which said, "You can't do it. You won't."

At the quintain the others ran the course handily while the spectators applauded. Nick surpassed himself. Not only did he miss the quintain entirely, but he dropped his lance and fell from the horse without even being hit by the sandbag.

Disgraced, ruined, he fled. There was a heavy silence behind him. Not even the pages jeered. Old Thomas made an awkward remark intended to console him, but it was worse than a tongue-lashing. It

142

showed Nick that Thomas considered him hopeless, an object of pity, far beyond any help. His complete misery was comforting, in an odd way; he felt that he no longer had to pretend, even to himself, that he would some day be a great fighting man like his father. He would never be anything but a big clumsy ox in armor—just what Sparrow had called him.

This realization did not help much, though. He sat on his cot in dumb suffering, his head in his hands, reliving over and over those awful moments in the tiltyard. The other squires came skylarking in, full of talk about the journey to Murrey, hoping that Alwain the Wolf would dare to attack so that they could win a glorious victory. John of Denby sat on Nick's bed, awkwardly trying to comfort him, but he shook off the friendly hand and John soon went away. Nick sat and suffered alone, refusing to leave squires' hall even for dinner, although the castle rang with the sounds of feasting and merriment.

In the evening Sir Bellamy came in. "I have no words of reproach for you, Nicholas," he said quietly. "I came to tell you that in the morning you will go with the others as escort to the boy."

"I?" Nick said with bitterness. "After playing the clown in the tiltyard? Do they need a fool?"

"It is Baron Odesham's wish. But, by St. Peter, keep out of trouble! Don't do anything, don't try anything—just ride quietly and see if you can stay on your horse!"

"Aye," Nick said, without spirit.

In the morning, after an almost sleepless night, he listlessly armed himself along with the others: short hauberk of scales made of boiled leather, steel cap, round shield, sword, and dagger. The other squires left him to himself, whether from pity or disgust he didn't know and didn't want to find out.

The company set out cheerfully—except for Nick—under smiling autumn skies. A young knight named Sir Eynaud was in command; besides Ralph, and his three servants, there were twelve men-at-arms and the six squires. Sir Eynaud led the way. Nick, his depression deepening with every step, brought up the rear. Some of the castle people followed for a short distance, and as they went through the village of Odesham the villagers came from their cottages to wave and cheer. Ralph accepted all this homage royally. Nick hardly noticed it; he was sunk too deep in his own gloomy thoughts.

They rode past the tilled fields and pasturelands, and into a tame sort of oak forest where swineherds kept watch over the Odesham pigs.

"Hello, Nick."

Startled, Nick glanced down. It was Ralph, an engaging figure in blue velvet, wearing a tiny sword—a ridiculous miniature of his father.

"I was sorry when you fell off the horse and they laughed," the boy announced. "I didn't laugh. I fall off my pony sometimes. It hurts. Did it hurt you, Nick?"

Nick managed a smile. "No, Ralph. At least not in the way you mean."

"I don't like to be laughed at, but my sisters often laugh at me. I don't think it's right to make fun of somebody who's doing the best he can. That's why I asked my father to let you come."

"Oh, you did, did you?" That explained a good many things.

Ralph nodded. "Father didn't want to let you come. He said—" The boy turned red, and added hastily, "I forget what he said." He reached up from his fat pony and patted Nick's arm. "Anyhow, I like you."

"Thank you," Nick said wryly.

Ralph chattered away eagerly. After a while Nick found himself talking freely and even laughing a little. The procession emerged from the oak forest and rode out onto a wide patch of wasteland. The riders were straggling, stretching out. One of the squires had brought a rebec, an instrument something like a guitar, and some sang as they rode along. Sir Eynaud was deep in talk with John of Denby. By their gestures, Nick felt sure they were discussing swordplay. The men-at-arms argued and swore; some of them played a game which involved guessing how many fingers another would show; some seemed asleep in their saddles.

Ralph's pony had hard going to match the stride of the horses, and Nick reined in to stay beside him. The road—actually only a half-defined trail—dipped downward gradually. Then the open wasteland gave way to trees, and they entered the Great Forest.

"Do you think Alwain the Wolf will attack us?" Ralph asked.

Nick pretended to consider. "Well, no. Not when he sees that big sword you're carrying. And all those men-at-arms."

"And you. You're bigger than the men-at-arms. And I think you're a better fighter too, Nick. In spite of falling off the horse."

The forest got thicker. Ancient trees cast a gloom over everything. There were half-heard scurryings and rustlings deep among the trees.

"Let's catch up to the others," Nick suggested.

Ralph pounded with his heels on his pony's sides, and peered half-fearfully, half-delightedly, into the green depths of the forest. It was very still.

And then, suddenly, it wasn't.

Nick heard a shrill whistle and a chorus of wild yelps. Ragged men dropped from branches onto the horsemen. Others darted from hiding places beside the pathway, flinging themselves on the men-at-arms. Horses whinnied and plunged.

Nick never remembered drawing his sword. He had made two vicious cuts before he really knew it, and two outlaws lay on the leaf-strewn path.

All at once he heard a frightened cry. A tall lanky man, from whose hat fluttered the tail of a wolf, had hauled Ralph from his pony and was running with him into the forest. Alwain the Wolf!

Just then an outlaw grabbed for Nick's bridle, and he kicked him away. Another swung a hatchet. Nick slammed him in the face with his shield, and he collapsed. Alwain was dodging and skipping among the trees, already almost out of sight. Nick spurred after him. The horse took a few steps, screamed, stumbled, and fell heavily.

Yelling incoherently, Nick jumped clear. Alwain was just in front of him now, but a burly outlaw in green sprang to bar Nick's path. Nick drove into him with his shoulder, and the outlaw folded up with a grunt.

There was only one thought in Nick's mind: Get the boy! He forgot that he was slow and clumsy, that he was in disgrace, that he didn't know how to handle a sword. With one hand he reached out, grabbed Alwain's leather jerkin, and yanked. The outlaw spun around and fell. Ralph rolled free. Nick scooped the boy up, thrust him between his own back and a tree, and prepared to give battle.

Alwain bounced to his feet, whipping out a long knife, and howled for reinforcements. Three other bandits raced up, and they all attacked at once.

Cut, parry, thrust, slice. Nick's arm seemed to move of its own accord. The long hours in the tiltyard were proving their worth. One outlaw, a skinny man with a long red nose, cut Nick's arm and then screeched as Nick's sword laid his face open. He hopped away, splattering blood.

Wild sounds of combat were coming from the roadway. As the sounds got closer, Nick heard the bellowed war-cry of Odesham. Another bandit reached out with a rusty sword. Nick made a lightning cut, and the bandit's hand, still clutching the rusty sword, fell to the ground.

The outlaws were retreating now, running away, pelting through the trees. The squires and men-at-arms, recovered from their surprise, were cutting the attackers down. Alwain cast one desperate look behind him, wavered, then turned to run. Nick dropped his sword and leaped after him. Wrapping his arms around the outlaw's waist, with a powerful heave he lifted him from his feet. The outlaw hung struggling and helpless in the air.

The men of Odesham came plunging through the woods. Except for the dead and the badly wounded, the bandits had vanished. John of Denby ran up. "The boy!" he shouted. "Where's the boy?"

"Here I am!" cried Ralph shrilly, waving his tiny sword. "Nick and I beat 'em!"

Nick, suddenly aware that he was still holding Alwain poised in mid-air, slammed him down so hard that the breath was jolted out of the outlaw's body. "Where's Sir Eynaud?" Nick asked.

"Dead," said John soberly. "A bandit dropped from the trees, pulled him from his horse, and stabbed him through the eye."

The others gathered around. Little Ralph was capering about wildly, beside himself with excitement. "Nick knocked 'em all over and killed 'em and cut their arms off! I saw him! Alwain ran away with me and Nick caught him, and we fought 'em all, we did—Nick and me!"

The outlaw on the ground was beginning to stir and gasp. "Is that Alwain the Wolf?" John asked.

"I suppose so," Nick answered gruffly. He didn't want to talk; he wanted to get off somewhere by himself, and think. A slow wonder was beginning to spread through him. Had *he,* slow-as-a-stick Nick, done all this? He couldn't believe it!

It seemed that Sparrow did not believe it, either. He sauntered up, looked down at Alwain and then up at Nick, and shook his head. "A most noble deed, my friends. Didn't I always tell you that our Nick was a very Lancelot?"

Nick exploded. "Hold your tongue, you posing popinjay! Sir Eynaud dead in the roadway, the boy kidnaped—and you chatter! I'm disgusted with the lot of you—asleep or singing instead of keeping watch, straggling along like a gaggle of geese instead of soldiers. I'll hear no more from any of you, least of all you, Hal Boutelier!"

"Ha, now—" Sparrow began, but John put a hand on his arm.

"Be quiet, Sparrow. Nick's right. We've gained small glory today, except for him. He's a better man than any of us."

"Never mind, John." Nick gestured to Alwain, who was sitting with his head on his arms. "Get him trussed up. He's coming with us."

"Better hang him now," a man-at-arms said.

"I said he's coming with us," Nick repeated. "Truss him up. The rest of you, back to horse. I don't think we'll be attacked again, but this time Ralph rides in the middle of the column. And we'll have outriders, too."

Nobody questioned his orders. Silently they went back to the road, mounted, and moved off. John rode Sir Eynaud's horse. The knight's body was laid over John's saddle, and the outlaw, looking despondent, was made to walk.

Nick rode beside Ralph. There was something here he couldn't understand exactly. Not yet, anyhow; it would take some thought. Was this all there was to it? When the outlaws attacked he had not thought of the advice of Sir Bellamy and Sir Jerome: Don't worry about yourself, think of others. Yet that was what had happened. Was it simply that he had been so concerned about little Ralph that there hadn't been time to worry about himself? Next time, there would probably be no child to rescue. Would he go back to being clumsy Nick, slow as a stick?

The idea was absurd, though he didn't know why. In a few days, he'd be running the quintain again, and he knew that he would hit it easily and fairly, but he didn't know how he knew this. What in the world was I afraid of? he asked himself. It's so simple! This must be that confidence that Sir Bellamy spoke of. It's a good feeling.

"You didn't listen," Ralph said accusingly.

Nick came to himself with a start. The cavalcade was almost out of the forest. Ahead stretched flat, open country, and in the distance was a strongly fortified manor house with a huddle of smaller houses around it. That would be their stop for the night. "Sorry," Nick said. "What did you say, Ralph?"

"When you're a knight," Ralph said, "can I be your squire?"

Nick laughed. "Why, youngster, that's up to your father."

"Oh," said the boy eagerly, "I think my father will like that!"

Privately, Nick thought so too.

The pages no longer called Nick "slow as a stick." He became a redoubtable knight, and took his part in the civil wars that raged when two people, Stephen and Matilda, both claimed the throne of England. Ralph did serve Nick as squire for a time, until he won his own golden spurs.

Meanwhile, the great age of knighthood passed its morning and came to full noon.

When people today hear the word "knight," they are likely to picture a man clad in plate armor from head to foot. Many books have been written about knights of the time of King Richard the Lion-Hearted, and illustrated with drawings of knights wearing armor that was not invented until four hundred years later.

In the great days of knighthood, as we have seen, knights wore hauberks of chain mail. At least, they did if they could afford them. Some got along with hauberks made of overlapping scales of thick leather, boiled and shaped, and these were not bad protection. Very little of that early armor has been preserved. Armor remaining from before the time of Columbus is rare, and anything earlier than the time of Joan of Arc, five hundred years ago, was saved almost by a miracle. Much of it was broken up by people who had no interest in relics. A lot more rusted away. And after all, in the early Middle Ages there probably were no more than a few thousand complete suits of mail in existence at any one time.

For years, an old-fashioned hauberk hung in the armory at Wyke-ford. The de Wykes were very proud of it, and pointed it out to visitors. It was the same hauberk that Drogo the Red had taken from Sir Rollo, that long-gone day in Normandy. Of course, the old hauberk was just a curiosity, not good for much any more. Its links were heavy and poorly made. The sleeves came only to the elbow. It was not good enough protection, and—worse—it was quite out of style.

The de Wykes had money enough to buy complete suits of mail for themselves. These were frighteningly expensive, for mail had to be imported from Italy or Spain.

The mail Roger wore in the Holy Land was a tremendous improvement on Drogo's. It was made of better metal, and the links were stronger, yet lighter. It was also more comfortable to wear, and easier to move around in. Furthermore, mail leggings and a mail coif had been added, and so Roger was protected from head to toe in a mesh of interlocking iron rings.

Even so, "comfortable" is a relative term. A suit of mail is not the sort of thing you would pick to relax in. If you would like to know how Roger felt, riding through the Holy Land on an August afternoon, you might try a little experiment: Wait until the very hottest day of a hot summer. Then put on an athletic sweat suit, or heavy trousers and sweater. Wrap a woolen scarf around your neck. Put on a football helmet. Pull on rubber boots or high overshoes. Borrow two sets of auto skid chains and wrap them around yourself. Get a baseball bat and the top from a galvanized iron trash can.

Then go out and run around the block for an hour or so, swinging the bat and shouting at the top of your lungs. If you want to be really thorough, have some friends take swats at you with their baseball bats. Of course the neighbors will think you're crazy, unless you explain that you're doing scientific research.

In Mark Twain's book *A Connecticut Yankee at King Arthur's Court,* the Yankee, Hank Morgan, is put into a suit of plate armor. Of course they didn't make suits of plate armor in King Arthur's time, but never mind—Mark Twain knew that. He was merely telling a story. Anyhow, the Yankee, sweating and unhappy in his plate and worried because there were no pockets in it, saw a knight of the Table Round come in. The Yankee said: "How stately he looked, and how tall and broad and grand. He had on his head a conical steel casque that only came down to his ears, and for a visor had only a narrow steel bar that extended down to his upper lip and protected his nose; and all the rest of him, from neck to heel, was flexible chain mail, trousers and all. But pretty much all of him was hidden under his outside garment, which of course was chain mail, as I said, and hung straight down from his shoulders to his ankles; and from his middle to the bottom, both before and behind, was divided, so he could ride and let the skirts hang down on each side..."

"I would have given a good deal for that ulster."

That's an excellent description of twelfth-century chain mail. The hauberk was usually shorter, about knee length, and the nosepiece was fairly rare by then—I don't know why; it seems like a sensible protection.

The Yankee didn't know when he was well off. He was far happier in his plate armor than he would have been in mail, pockets or no pockets. A hauberk like the one he described would weigh from sixty to ninety pounds, and its entire weight hung from the shoulders. The muscles which had to support all that weight also had to be used to swing heavy weapons.

Iron is iron, after all—not cloth—and there is no way of fitting a coat made of links of metal. It bunches up under the armpits and at the elbows. A knight laced up in a hauberk, with a padded gambeson under it, could hardly put his arms down close to his sides or bend his elbows enough to feed himself a spoonful of food. The only way he could handle his sword was by wide, sweeping cuts.

When you come right down to it, the human body isn't constructed for wearing clothes efficiently, except maybe a hat. Even such a simple thing as a cloak presents problems. If you make a poncho kind of garment, with a hole in the middle for your head, your arms aren't free. A cloak flung over the shoulders looks dramatic and impressive, but it drags down at the back, and if you fasten it at the neck it chokes you. Sleeves were always a tremendous problem for clothing makers. Buttons are a comparatively recent invention. As late as the time of the Three Musketeers, about three hundred years ago, men held up their breeches with a system of lashings called points. And not even today have we hit on a completely satisfactory way of keeping stockings from falling down.

The art of making armor was ancient even when Sir Roger rode against the Saracens. Primitive men had armor made of thick skins, or small bones fastened together, or even of wickerwork. In the days of the Greeks and Romans, armor-making was developed to a high point. Their armor was well designed and some of it was beautiful, but it was a long way from being perfect. They could have designed armor to protect the whole body as well as the vital parts, but it would have been useless. They were foot soldiers, and the armor of a foot soldier has to be light enough so that he can march all day and still carry his weapons and baggage. Greek and Roman armor could ward off arrows or turn the edge of a barbarian sword. But the soldier's thighs and arms were bare, and a wound in the leg can put a man out of action as fast as one in the stomach. The neck was unprotected too. And even at best, their armor was so light that a heavy spear or battle-ax could go right through it.

Of course, they carried shields, which are actually movable armor. Handling a shield is quite a trick. You don't just crouch down behind

154

it and hope for the best. You try to outguess your enemy, figure out where he is going to strike next, and have your shield there. The Greeks used huge, heavy shields. The Roman shield was smaller and built more scientifically. In the Dark Ages, men carried shields with "bosses," projecting knobs or spikes of metal which could be used as weapons, in a pinch.

Then came the Man on Horseback, and at once it became obvious that a fighting man could carry more armor. Rather than plod along on foot, he could sit in a saddle, more or less comfortably, and let the horse do the work. Also, since the new tactics depended on the terrific shock of a heavy cavalry charge, he needed all the protection he could get. So armor got heavier and heavier, more and more complete, until by the time Roger rode against the Saracens, knights were almost completely covered.

Once hauberks had been improved, shields did not have to be as large as the one Drogo carried at Hastings. They became lighter and more maneuverable, and as armor got still better, the shields got smaller and smaller until they disappeared entirely.

A knight of Roger's day stood an excellent chance of coming back alive from a battle. The ordinary light arrows of that time couldn't hurt him, unless they happened to hit him in the face. His mail would turn the blow of a sword. But men realized that mail was still far from perfect armor. It was heavy, and restricted the movements of its wearer. A direct hit from a battle-ax would smash the links into the wound. A lance point would go through mail. And mail did not have a smooth, glancing surface; a weapon's point was likely to catch in the links.

Long before Roger was born, armorers had begun experimenting with plate to reinforce the mail. They made "plastrons," which were breastplates, and "pauldrons," something like a football player's shoulder pads. But they ran into difficulties, too. A sheet of steel would not bend, and chain mail, for all its awkwardness, would. It was easy enough to design pieces of plate for the thighs and shins or the forearms, but when it came to fashioning pieces which would allow the wearer to move freely and bend his joints, that was something else again.

They kept on experimenting. New weapons were turning up. The light francisc of the Franks had long vanished, replaced by a heavy battle-ax. Swords got longer, heavier, sharper. So did lances. The ancient scramasax was gone, but in its place was the glaive, or falchion, a heavy single-edged blade. Many preferred it to the sword for chopping through links of mail. The deadly crossbow, or arbalest, was becoming popular. To their dismay, knights found that a bolt from an arbalest would pierce mail easily. They tried to get the weapon outlawed, without much success.

The face was a very vulnerable spot; nobody had yet hit on the idea of movable visors. Instead of the simple steel casque of early Norman times, knights began wearing an enormous, heavy pot helmet, or helm, which looked like nothing so much as the end of a hot-water boiler. Roger had one that weighed eighteen pounds and was fastened to his hauberk by a chain. His father had given it to him the day he was made a knight, but he hated it and rarely wore it, except in tournaments. It was an uncomfortable thing to wear. The whole weight came on his head. The helm rested on a circlet of straw bound in cloth, which he put on over his mail coif. The helm was provided with a narrow slit through which he could see—although not very well—and some holes to admit air, but Roger always felt half-smothered when he wore it. On top was a ring to which a crest could be fastened—a favor from a lady, perhaps, or a heraldic animal made of leather or light wood. Roger didn't wear a crest, either, but he had his own reason for that.

As already mentioned, Roger, and his family before him, lived in a fortified manor house. It was not a castle, although it had a wall around it which could be defended, and the house itself was built partly of thick stones. Roger spent a good deal of his time in castles, as part of a lord's meinie, and so he was always glad to get back to Wykeford, because there he was master and not merely a member of a lord's household. But there was more to it than that. Wykeford would have been miserably uncomfortable by our standards—cold, drafty, bare, damp—but it was considerably better than a castle. Most of them were built as fortresses first and dwelling-places second. Whatever primitive ideas of comfort the builders may have had were sacrificed for strength.

Drogo spent his early years in a castle belonging to a minor Norman noble. It was made of wood, just as the house of his ancestor Huberic had been, centuries before. The Norman castle was perched on a hill; around it was a ditch bridged by planks, which could be removed if necessary. Inside the ditch was a high, stout palisade of pointed logs. It was bigger and stronger than Huberic's, though not much different, after all.

The first Norman castles in England were built after the same plan, but it wasn't long before the barons began building of stone. Then castles got bigger and more elaborate, with walls inside walls, stronger and higher keeps, better-planned defenses. Round towers replaced square ones because they were stronger. Architects even thought of such practical improvements as staircases designed to give the defenders room to swing their weapons, at the same time that attackers would be hampered by the stone walls.

Probably the first thing that would strike you, if you went to live in a twelfth-century castle, would be the lack of privacy. There was literally no place where a person could go and be by himself. Even the lord probably slept in the same room with a dozen other people. Next, you would notice the clammy chill—if the weather were cold —and the breezes that blew through every room. Then your attention would be caught by the smells. Some pleasant, from the kitchens. But most were unpleasant, from the moat, which was actually an open sewer; or the stables; or the kennels; or the garbage on the midden-heap; or the pigsty; or the mews where the hawks and falcons were kept; or the general indifference to dirt. You would doubtless also be surprised by the scarcity of furniture. The lord and lady had beds, and perhaps some high-ranking members of the meinie did too, but almost everybody else slept on the floor, on straw. There would be some chests for storing household treasure, clothes, and linens. Boards were set up on trestles to serve as tables, and there would be an array of stools or benches and perhaps a couple of chairs. There might even be a few other small odds and ends. But that was about all.

Two hundred years later, in Chaucer's time, all this would be changed. By 1360, ordinary people were living on a scale of comfort which would have made Roger's eyes open wide, although it seems meager enough to us.

No, a castle was not the place to go for solid comfort, rest, and relaxation. But then, people knew very little about comfort in those days, and they didn't miss it, which was just as well, perhaps.

One of the things we associate with the days of knights and armor is the custom of heraldry—the system of badges by which certain knights, or certain families, were known.

Roger's shield—the one scarred by a Saracen scimitar—was red, with a diagonal stripe of white, and on the white stripe the picture of an ancient brass lamp. To describe it in the special language of heraldry: "Gules, a bend argent, bearing an antique lamp, or." "Or" means gold.

Centuries later, men who studied heraldry decreed that it was bad form to put one metal on another. Gold on silver, they said, was shocking. In Roger's day nobody had ever thought of such a thing. And the later de Wykes said their blazon, or badge, had always been a gold lamp on a silver bend, and that was the way it was going to stay.

158

Drogo the Red knew nothing of heraldry. He took a red shield from Sir Rollo, and liked it because it matched his red hair. When it was smashed he got another one like it, and that's all there was to Drogo's heraldry. Red shields thereafter became the custom in the de Wyke family.

In Drogo's day, kings and princes had begun to use devices or special colors which came to be identified with them. Some time later, the custom spread to lesser nobles, and eventually to ordinary knights. It was a good idea, and made things easier all around.

Let's suppose, for example, that you were a man-at-arms in the meinie of a knight named Sir Thopas. Of course you would not know how to read. And in battle, Sir Thopas and his men might be only part of a very large army. Remember, too, that all knights in armor look pretty much alike, even without helms covering their faces. If

159

you became separated from Sir Thopas, how would you find him again? You might have a long search, for you would probably discover that few of the men around you knew him by sight. But if you knew that Sir Thopas' blazon was a yellow eagle on a black field, you'd only have to watch for that pennon or a shield bearing that sign, and you'd have your man.

The early blazons were simple. Most of them seem to have been chosen for no particular reason except, perhaps, that they could be easily recognized. The oldest families still bear uncomplicated stripes and checks, chevrons and crosses.

But diffculties arose. It sometimes happened that two families chose the same blazon, through pure coincidence. That always meant a lawsuit, sometimes open warfare. There were more common problems. Suppose a certain lord had three sons. His shield and pennons bore his blazon: horizontal stripes of blue and white—"barry azure and argent." But if all the family carried the same shield, how could anyone tell which was which? And suppose the three sons all had sons. Before long, there would be fifty people all entitled to bear "barry azure and argent." And if there were a civil war, with part of the family fighting on one side, part on the other, imagine the confusion!

Cousins, nephews, grandsons, all wanted to use the same family blazon, and matters became increasingly complicated. Finally, it was decided that umpires, called heralds, would assign blazons and adjudge disputes. They set up rules which everybody had to follow. They also developed their own language. It doesn't mean much to us now. Of course today we still frequently see coats of arms of one kind or another, but these are usually for a soft drink or an expensive hotel, and they have no standing at all with the College of Heralds. Some people in the United States, perhaps with a streak of snobbery, do affect coats of arms. And Europeans, especially the British, still set a good deal of store by them.

160

Needless to say, only noble families were allowed to display coats of arms in the old days. If you were a merchant—it didn't matter how rich you were—you could not have your own coat of arms, although the guild you belonged to could. A person who was allowed to display his own blazon was known as an "armiger"—one who has the right to bear arms.

Here is another sample of heraldic language: "Gules, a fess dancetty vert, a pierced mullet argent thereon"—meaning a red shield with a zigzag band of green across it horizontally, and on the green band a white star with a hole in it. Many of the terms used in heraldry are French. It would take too long, and mean too little, to go into detail about all the charges and ordinaries, the crests and supporters, the mottoes and tinctures, and the various other technical expressions. It would take even longer, and be even duller, to talk about all the rules and regulations.

Some families adopted a coat of arms similar to their name. The Shelleys, for example, might choose a shield bearing seashells. Something like that happened to the de Wykes. They had always carried red shields. Roger's grandfather, Robert, had one that was red with a white stripe vertically down the center. Roger's father, Nicholas, used a red shield with a white diamond in it. To both of them, their shields were just red and white; the design had no special significance.

Then, one winter night in the manor house at Wykeford, Robert and Nicholas were watching little Roger playing on the floor in front of the fire. They began discussing, as fathers and grandfathers will, what kind of shield the little boy would bear when he grew up and became a knight.

Nicholas, proud of his young son, said he thought it would be a good idea if the de Wykes chose a design and stuck with it. He said the great lords were doing just that. Robert agreed, and suggested his shield, but Nicholas preferred his own with the diamond on it.

161

They argued, in a friendly way, and finally decided on a compromise: a white diagonal on a red field. So new was the science of heraldry that they didn't even call it a "bend." They sent for one of the manor servants, a cripple named Adam who did whatever painting jobs were to be done, and Adam decorated a new shield for them.

Nicholas was dissatisfied. It looked too plain, he said; the de Wykes ought to have something more distinctive. They discussed various ideas, to no avail. Then Nicholas looked at little four-year-

old Roger, who was playing with his favorite toy, a battered, broken old brass lamp from Byzantium. The boy liked to pretend it was an armored knight, and would stage terrific battles between the lamp and an old iron hinge.

Nicholas laughed and took the lamp away from his son, ignoring the child's howls. "The very thing!" he said. A lamp had a wick; the family name was de Wyke; the pun meant nothing in Norman-French and was pretty farfetched even in English, but it was an idea.

Why not have a picture of the brass lamp on the de Wyke shield?

Robert agreed, provided they could find someone who could paint it. They did. Not Adam, who was far too clumsy, but the manor chaplain, who turned out a very respectable picture. Later on, the armorer sawed a relief of the lamp from a strip of brass and fastened it to the shield with rivets.

So the de Wyke coat of arms was born. Neither Robert nor Nicholas remembered to tell Roger how the blazon had originated, and he accepted it without question. Generations later, descendants of the de Wyke family made up fanciful tales to account for the lamp. For hundreds of years they believed that King Henry II had awarded the blazon to the family for great deeds of valor. The red, they said, stood for courage. The white stood for trustworthiness, and the lamp for wisdom. Nearly two centuries after Roger fought in the Holy Land, a de Wyke made up a Latin motto which meant "Wisdom with Valor with Trust."

Still later, the de Wykes, then prosperous members of the lesser nobility, sported an ornate coat of arms with a crest, two supporters, and all the paraphernalia. Then finally there was no one left named de Wyke, and the blazon was forgotten by everyone except scholars who peered at dusty old records.

But nobody, however, ever knew the story of little Roger and the brass lamp.

The Great Hall of Odesham Castle was hot and stuffy in spite of its size. It was only a short time after midday, but torches were burning—the small slit windows could never let in enough light—and a smell of grease from the torches and from the dinner which had just been cleared away hung heavy in the air. In the vast room were about a hundred people, counting servants, and all were laughing and chattering. In the musicians' gallery, Baron Hugues' five-man orchestra was tuning up.

Young Sir Roger de Wyke hardly heard them. He was deafened by the talk and dazed by the brilliant flashes of yellow, red, blue, purple, and gold of the guests' costumes. He was dressed no less gaudily himself; his tunic was bright blue, with the golden lamp badge of the de Wykes on his chest; his surcoat was red, and his soft leather shoes were yellow. Yet in spite of all this splendor, Roger was acutely miserable. He stood quietly, and he hoped unnoticed, under the musicians' gallery, listening in dumb agony to the plunking and scraping overhead, and wished he were anywhere but here.

It was not the stuffiness, or the heat, or the greasy smell. All these he was used to and hardly noticed. It was simply that he was twenty years old, made a knight only the week before, and he knew he was as clumsy as a trained bear when it came to dancing. He also had the idea that every eye was on him. This wasn't so, of course. None of Baron Hugues' guests paid him the slightest attention. Why should they waste their time on an unknown, when so many of the country's most renowned knights and nobles, so many of the country's most beautiful women, were gathered at Castle Odesham for the first great tournament of the year?

Roger had looked forward to his first tournament since that distant day when he began the long training which finally won him his golden spurs. Now the time was here. Tomorrow he would meet these famed knights in the lists outside the castle, but it was not the thought of fighting in a tournament that made him unhappy. No, not even though he knew that such famed champions as Sir Girard of Stoke, Sir Anselm Hammer-Fist, and Sir Fulke le Manz were taking part. He'd go against them and do his best. No one could do more.

The thing that had thrown Roger into a panic was the fact that half the people in the Great Hall were women.

This should not have worried him at all. Part of his training for knighthood was supposed to have been learning about courtly love and romance—how to write songs, to play the lute, to dance, to exchange bright conversation with girls. By now, he was supposed to have chosen a ladylove who would be the object of his undying affection, and whose favor he would wear in battle.

Somehow it hadn't worked out that way, at all. Roger had spent his apprenticeship in the meinie of grim old Sir Robert Yarrow, in a lonely castle near the wild Welsh border. This place, selected by his father, was an excellent choice as far as making Roger a fighting man went. But for the gayer side of chivalry—no. There had been some women at Yarrow: Sir Robert's gray-haired wife, nearly as grim as her husband; their daughter, the Lady Ellen, a sad-faced, quiet widow of thirty; and a few featherbrained ladies-in-waiting, who had giggled and made inane remarks whenever Roger had tried to be courtly.

Oh, he had tried, all right. But Roger's thick fingers were made for the hilt of a sword, not for plucking lute-strings; and his muscular legs, at home on a horse, seemed to go in all directions at once when he tried to dance. As for writing songs, he had trouble enough writing his own name; and whenever he had attempted to sing, old Sir Robert looked grimmer than ever and gave audible thanks for his deafness.

Now, far removed from that austere warrior's castle, he was in the gay, brilliant home of Baron Hugues, in the midst of the most courtly company in the kingdom of England. He watched in despair as a young squire—not even a knight—walked slowly in front of him, twirling a flower and exchanging light talk with a pretty girl in silver brocade. He tried to picture himself in the squire's place, and shrank back farther under the gallery.

Then he felt a hand on his shoulder. It was Sir Percivale, the baron's oldest son, known as Bonfilz or "good son," for the love and respect he gave his father. Everyone liked Sir Percivale, a handsome, friendly, intelligent man—liked and pitied him, because he had lost an arm in a tournament some years before.

"Ha, Roger! Hiding in a corner, with the hall full of lovely women you haven't met! Come along, now. I won't have the son of my father's oldest friend neglected."

Roger tried to say that he was perfectly happy and would much rather be neglected than not, but Sir Percivale's hand propelled him out into the laughing crowd. Dumbly, he let himself be pushed. Percivale leaned close to his ear. "I know how you feel, Roger. It won't be so bad after a while. Come, man! You can't moon in a corner all your life." He steered Roger toward a knight and two girls who were laughing together.

"Friends, have you met Sir Roger de Wyke, son of Sir Nicholas, who is here for the tournament? Tomorrow will be his first passage at arms."

Percivale mentioned names. Roger bowed mechanically, though he hadn't heard a word. He had been struck dumb and foolish by

the sight of one of the girls, a slim black-haired sprite who was the most beautiful thing he had ever seen in his life. Awkwardly, he recovered from his bow and stood trying to think of something to say.

The knight, a man some years older than Roger, bore a badge showing a heron, or some kind of water bird. Finally, conscious that he was staring at the black-haired girl, Roger turned his eyes toward the man. He disliked him on sight. The knight had a disdainful, arrogant face, looked with amusement and contempt on Roger, and worse, was toying with the sleeve of the lovely black-haired girl. A heron, white on a green field. Automatically, Roger's mind supplied the identification: le Manz. This, then, must be the redoubtable Sir Fulke of that house, the acknowledged champion of the lists, undefeated master of lance and sword.

"Your first tournament, Sir—ah, Sir Roger?" Fulke said with a smile that was half sneer. "You're a brave novice, to enter against such champions as will be in the lists tomorrow."

"Yes, I am," Roger said idiotically, then realized how bad that sounded. "I mean—no, I'm not brave, it's just that—" He floundered into silence, aware that he was making a complete fool of himself.

The bewitching dark girl smiled enchantingly. "He's not brave, Fulke. You see, he says so himself. So you have nothing to fear from him."

Fulke threw back his head and laughed. "It had not occurred to me, Lady Yvonne, that I had anything to fear from this young man."

She leaned roguishly toward Fulke. "Ah, but defeat often comes from the least expected quarter."

"When I'm near you, my lady, I expect defeat. And your eyes always defeat me. Or your smile. Alas, you are too well armed, Lady Yvonne."

This was the sort of talk which always drove Roger to despair. To be able to carry on that kind of conversation with Yvonne, he would cheerfully have entered the lists weaponless. But he could only stand like a clod, hating Fulke le Manz.

"Have you been to Odesham before, Sir Roger?" a timid voice asked.

He had forgotten the other girl. Startled, he turned his eyes toward her. Certainly she was unexciting by comparison with Lady Yvonne. She was small, with a round face and light brown hair. Her eyes were blue, like Yvonne's, but trusting and friendly instead of challenging.

"Yes, my lady," Roger said. At least this was a simple question that he could answer. "My father and Baron Hugues are old comrades in arms. I have been here many times."

"This is the first time for me," she said. The remark didn't seem to require an answer, but Roger felt that he must say something. Especially since Fulke and the Lady Yvonne had gone off somewhere, without even bothering to say a word to him, and he was alone with the girl. What was her name, anyhow?

She seemed to sense his difficulty. "Agatha Fitzwarin," she said, and smiled. "No, don't apologize, Sir Roger. You are not the first knight so smitten by my beautiful cousin that he did not hear my name."

He started to say something, then gave up gratefully, and suggested that they walk. She put her fingertips on his sleeve and they wound through the crowd, which was beginning to form lines for the first dance.

"Should we—" Agatha said, indicating the dancers.

"I'm sorry, Lady Agatha. I've tried, really I have. But I could no more dance than I could get up with the musicians and scrape a viol. I'm not at home with women, my lady. You may have noticed." He grinned, feeling a slight surprise that he could grin.

Agatha gave him an answering smile. "I don't really want to dance anyhow. It's hot in here. Let's go into the courtyard."

They made their way out of the Great Hall, passing by the elders who sat watching the dancers. As they went, Roger kept his eyes on the graceful figure of Lady Yvonne, who was weaving through the figures of the dance with Fulke. He knew it was discourteous to watch one woman when he was with another, but he couldn't help it. Oh, but she was beautiful! If only he could be there, instead of Fulke le Manz, his hand over hers! If Agatha Fitzwarin noticed, she gave no sign.

It was only a short while before a red-haired squire came to claim Agatha for the dancing. Roger had been glad of her company, but he was equally glad to see her go. Just now, he wanted to be alone. He climbed to the top of the keep, where the guard saluted him respectfully, and gazed out over the rolling fields and forests. He didn't think of Agatha at all; he thought of Fulke and of Lady Yvonne. Fulke he hated. Of that he was sure. Yvonne—well, he had heard plenty of talk about love, but he didn't know. He would have jumped headfirst from the battlement if Yvonne had asked him to. Was that love? Was that what the minstrels sang about?

Roger had never had a ladylove. Until now. He knew that other knights had ladies and wore their favors into battle—a glove or a scarf, knotted on the lance or helm. He gulped. Did he dare ask her for such a favor? The thought scared him half to death. But it was Yvonne, or it was no one. That, Roger knew well...

That night as he was trying to sleep on the rushes and skins spread on the floor of his tiny tent, which was set up outside the castle walls, Roger reached up from time to time to pat, cautiously, a small piece of linen. It was a sleeve from one of Yvonne's gowns. Yvonne had given it to him. To *him*, Roger de Wyke! How had he ever had the effrontery to ask her? It had taken more courage than he knew he possessed. But there it was—a plain piece of linen, not very decorative. He had hoped for a velvet glove or a scarf—but after all it was hers, Yvonne's, and that was surely enough. Roger drifted off to sleep and a confused dream in which he was attacking Fulke le Manz with a huge linen sleeve tied to a musician's viol.

The knights' tents, or pavilions, were astir before sunrise. Roger's squire brought him a horn of wine, bread and bacon, and a dish of beans, and stood over him to see that he ate. It did no good to protest that he was not hungry. Pol, the squire, was a grizzled middle-aged man who had spent his life in the service of the de Wykes, and he had no intention of letting Roger go into battle with an empty stomach.

Then came the business of arming. Pol, as a good squire should, had gone over every piece of Roger's harness the night before. The hauberk shone. The surcoat was new. The shield was bright and well padded with sheepskin. As he fastened Roger's new gilt spurs, Pol's eyes were moist. "You carry the honor of the de Wykes today, boy," he said. There was no formal "sir" when they were alone. "I taught you your first sword stroke when you where three. A little wooden sword you had then. You've a real one now, even if it is blunted for the tourney. Use it well, and remember good Sir Robert's teachings."

Roger gripped his squire's shoulder, then went from the pavilion to mount. During the night it had rained and the air was fresh and cool. Knights' pennons waved gaily. The lists, which occupied the space between the castle's outer wall and the castle itself, were crowded with gentlefolk, tradesmen, villagers, servants, all keeping up an endless babble. Roger felt as if he were on display. The crowd milled around, gawking and pointing at him, exchanging remarks on his appearance and his probable luck in the coming contests, as if he couldn't hear a word.

Roger mounted, and joined the procession of knights who were to take part in the tourney. To one side of the lists, in a brightly decorated stand, sat Baron Hugues and Sir Percivale, with a number of other knights and a perfect flower-garden of ladies. As the combatants rode slowly around the lists, lowering their lance points in turn before the stand, Roger kept his eyes constantly on one particular lady. Yvonne, sitting close beside Sir Percivale, gave him a tiny smile. Roger was a little disappointed; some of the other ladies were waving kerchiefs and cheering loudly for their favorites, and after all, wasn't he wearing her favor?

Her favor! Roger nearly reined his horse around. Dolt, idiot, fool! In the excitement of arming, he had forgotten to knot it on his lance! No wonder Lady Yvonne, lovely Lady Yvonne, seemed distant!

As soon as the ceremonial procession had completed the circle, the knights dispersed to their pavilions to await their turn in the lists.

The plan of the tourney was simple enough. Certain knights had been invited by Baron Hugues to make up the "castle party," and they were open to challenge by any of the others. There would be single combats today and tomorrow; on the final day, as was usual, there would be a great melee, with the castle party against all the others.

Baron Hugues' second son, Henry, a beefy man with a considerable reputation as a fighter, was the leader of the castle party. It included Sir Fulke, and a number of other tournament veterans. The "visitors' party" was about equal in numbers and ability. There were all kinds of knights on both sides. Some, like Fulke, were wealthy men, courtiers, landholders, the best of the nation's warriors. Some belonged to that group of knights who made their living by going from one tourney to another, picking up what they could in the way of ransom—dangerous, seasoned, professional fighters. Some were merely ordinary knights seeking a good time, good journeyman combatants with nothing in particular to make them stand out. Some, like Roger himself, were novices, young knights in their first competition.

Roger reined up before his small pavilion. "Listen!" he said. "I—"

"Now mind," Pol said, paying no attention. "It's up to you to challenge, and you want to make a wise choice. It won't do any good to break lances with another youngster like yourself. And—"

"Be quiet!" Roger roared. "Where's the Lady Yvonne's sleeve?"

"Whatever you do," said Pol, engrossed in his thoughts, "don't ring the shield of someone like Fulke le Manz, who'll spill you on the ground."

Roger forgot the sleeve for a moment. He felt himself bristle. "Fulke le Manz? Spill me on the ground? That perfumed chatter-box?"

"You heard me. Perfumed he may be, but he's the most dangerous man in England with the long stick. Steer clear of him. Leave Fulke to one of those professional jousters. They'll be willing to gamble— Fulke is worth a rich ransom—but you've no business in the lists with him. Not yet."

Roger grunted. He had his own ideas about Fulke le Manz but he had learned to rely on Pol's judgment, and the thought of being spilled ignominiously on his first passage at arms was appalling. He thought of Yvonne watching him rolling on the ground, and shuddered.

"Pick someone like Bertran de Saint-Haye," Pol went on. "He never has amounted to much and he never will, but everyone knows him, and to knock him over is worth something. Besides, Bertran is the best-natured man in the world and always makes friends with the men who spill him."

Roger laughed. "All right, Pol. Bertran it is. But I want—"

From the lists came the roar of the crowd. There was a thudding of hoofs, a crash. Pol cocked an experienced ear. "Badly run," he said. "Two glancing blows. Youngsters. Now remember what I've told you a thousand times about minding your shield. A shield well held can make all the difference between—"

Roger reached down and gave his old friend an affectionate buffet on the ear. "Lessons are all over, Pol. If I haven't learned by now, I never will."

"You're right, boy. Take your lance." He handed up the twelve-foot shaft, spiraled in white and red. This was a tournament lance, with one of the new crow's-foot heads instead of a sharp point, to minimize injuries. Then Pol handed up the big, heavy pot helmet. "I know you don't like this, boy, but it's time to put it on."

"Not yet. I've been trying to ask you, Pol. Where's the sleeve? Lady Yvonne's sleeve?"

"Oh." Pol ducked into the tent and came out in a moment with the piece of linen. "Properly dazzled by her, aren't we?" He peered at the piece of linen closely, and his forehead wrinkled.

"What's the matter now?" Roger demanded.

Pol looked up, an odd expression on his brown face. "Boy, this is a queer bit of cloth for a fine lady to have for a sleeve. More fit for a kitchen wench, I'd say."

Roger felt a wave of anger. "Hold your tongue! Give me the sleeve!"

He grabbed it, and awkwardly tried to knot it into the ring on top of his helmet. Kitchen wench! Old friend or no, Pol needed to be taught a lesson!

And yet—grudgingly—half his mind told him it *was* a coarse piece of cloth, a drab, poorly-sewed thing. Little as he knew of fine ladies and their clothing, a dark suspicion crossed his mind. Instantly he stifled it as an unworthy thought for a knight. A little self-consciously, he raised the favor to his lips.

The suspicion returned. The sleeve didn't *smell* like Lady Yvonne, all sweet perfume. It smelled of sweat and grease.

He remembered Yvonne, laughing and leaning on the handsome Fulke. He remembered the tone of her voice as she bade him wait while she fetched a sleeve from her "best gown." Yes, that was what she had said. "A favor worthy of such a gallant knight"—she had said that, too.

Roger might be green, but he was not stupid. He had been bedazzled by the lovely Yvonne—but now he knew. His adored lady had played a mean, unforgivable trick on him. And by now, undoubtedly, the entire castle knew that Sir Roger de Wyke was going into the tourney wearing the sleeve of a kitchen wench, and probably an old fat one at that. For a man to have offered such an insult would have meant instant challenge, but what could he do to a woman? He felt shamed, angry, bitter.

"What's the matter, boy?" Pol asked anxiously.

"Nothing. I just found out something, Pol. I found out that there are lessons which can't be learned in the tiltyard."

He settled the helmet on his head—without Lady Yvonne's "favor" —and made his way slowly through the crowds pressing in close to the lists. Another course was being run. Roger listened to the rising volume of shouts as hoofs thundered on the turf, the clash of lance against shield, the heavy thud as a body hit the earth, the delirious whoops of the spectators. A good course, fairly run and fairly won. Half his mind told him that, while the other half grew darker with anger every minute.

It must have been Fulke le Manz who had put Yvonne up to such a nasty joke. Vain, sneering Fulke, who didn't bother to hide his disdain for a young comrade in arms!

Just ahead rose the bright tents of the castle party. In front of each one, on a staff, hung a painted shield. There was one he didn't recognize. There was the checked black-and-silver of Bertran de Saint-Haye, and the knight himself beside it, smiling. And there was the heron blazon of Fulke le Manz.

Roger knew what he was going to do, in spite of Pol, in spite of his own better judgment. Hardly looking at the other shields, he reined in his horse in front of the tent with the heron shield, lowered his lance, and dealt the shield a blow that knocked it off its rack and sent it clattering to the ground.

A face appeared in the tent's opening, the face of Fulke. The older knight's lips curled in a smile as he saw who had challenged him. "Ah! The young Sir—Roger, is it?" He came from the tent, tall and strong in gleaming mail. "The knight who admits he isn't very brave! Whose favor do you wear, Sir Roger?"

"No lady's favor, Sir Knight." In spite of the anger boiling inside him, Roger was determined to be courteous. He inclined his head. "I await your pleasure."

A little knot of knights and squires had gathered around the tent. As Roger rode slowly off, he heard Fulke say something and an answering laugh. Bertran de Saint-Haye, his red, round face worried, blinked up at him. "What did you do that for, young sir? Your first tournament and you challenge Fulke le Manz!" He shook his head.

"I hope, Sir Bertran, to run a course with you later," Roger said, and the other knight smiled.

"Why, 'twould be a pleasure! If—" He paused and cast a glance at Fulke's tent, to which a squire was already leading a huge bay destrier. "If Sir Fulke—" He coughed. "Why did you challenge him, boy?"

"A personal matter, Sir Bertran," Roger said, riding on.

He circled the lists to the visitors' side. A clarion blew, and he heard the herald calling, in a hoarse voice, the names of the next contestants: Sir Fulke le Manz and Sir Roger de Wyke. Pol came running up, scowling. "Have you lost your wits, boy? What did I tell you just now? What demon possessed you to—"

"Peace," Roger said. "I did what I had to do."

Surprisingly, Pol grinned and ducked his head. "Ah, well, I thought you would. Mind, I still think you're daft." He sighed. "I would have done the same." He hovered like a mother hen, testing saddle girth and bridle, dropping the lance to the earth to try its soundness, hauling at the guige, the shield strap. Roger submitted patiently.

Then, suddenly, he was all alone, sitting his destrier in the glare of sunlight, facing the long green strip of the lists. He felt, rather than saw or heard, the hundreds of people who watched. The marshal of the lists sat motionless on his saddle, his baton held horizontally before him. When it dropped, the combatants would ride.

At the other end of the lists appeared Sir Fulke, at that distance small and insignificant, a doll in green and silver. Roger found his place and sat quietly. The crowd grew still. Somehow, they sensed that here was something more than the ordinary game.

Roger's anger was gone, and his nervousness. He felt serene and confident. The lance was familiar in his hand, and the heavy shield was exactly like all the other shields he had carried throughout his years of training. His destrier stood calm, although Roger could feel the shivers of impatience running through the mighty body. Roger's mind was empty. He was concentrating on the baton in the marshal's hand.

It fell. He clapped spurs to the destrier, and with a powerful surge the horse swung into his gallop. Almost by itself Roger's lance moved down, halfway to position, held there until he couched it for the impact. Instinctively he assumed the best position to withstand the coming shock—feet firm in the stirrups, body slightly crouched, eyes just over the level of the shield.

Fulke was no longer a doll, but a man on a horse which was drumming toward him at full gallop. Then a frightening thing happened.

A wild surge of fear and doubt went through Roger. He could remember nothing. The lance felt strange and awkward, the shield clumsy. He lost his feeling of oneness with the horse beneath him.

The thought flashed through his mind: I shall be badly hurt, like Percivale Bonfilz; maybe killed—I'll never unhorse Fulke.

Keep the lance steady, he told himself desperately, keep the lance steady!

He had never known such a shock. He couldn't breathe. Crazy lights danced before his eyes. He did not know where he was. A roaring filled his ears. His arms were numb. Then, slowly, he realized he was still in the saddle, carrying the shattered butt of a splintered lance.

He didn't unhorse me! his mind cried.

His mind cleared. He pulled the destrier into a turn. Neither had Fulke been unhorsed. The green and silver knight was reining in at the far end of the lists. He, too, carried a shattered lance.

It was all to do over again. Neither had gained an advantage.

Time lost its meaning. A new lance was thrust into his hand by Pol, who talked urgently and meaninglessly. The baton dropped. The destrier surged forward. The green and silver doll grew into a menacing, faceless figure. The world exploded.

Roger came to himself back at the end of the lists, with Pol, worried and half-hysterical, thrusting still another lance into his hand.

"Never have I seen such a shock...Are you all right, boy? This time decides it. What a course, what a course! You're doing fine, fine!"

"I'm all right," Roger said. And, he suddenly realized, he *was* all right. His nose was bleeding—he could feel the warm drops—his left arm was numb, he felt dizzy and sick. But he was all right, he was fine, he could run the third course with Fulke.

The baton dropped. His daze had passed. Coldly, he watched as Fulke approached. The point of Fulke's lance came down. Too far. A trap—he would raise it just before the shock. Roger held his own lance awkwardly, intentionally so, the point aiming at the outer

edge of Fulke's shield. At the same time he leaned over, the merest trifle, holding his own shield out a little to give Fulke a bad target.

The riders were nearly upon each other. Just as he suspected! Fulke's lance rose, aiming for the center of Roger's shield. Roger pulled his shield in and straightened in the saddle. He straightened his own point too.

The heron badge filled his eyes. The riders came together.

Suddenly Roger became aware that the roaring was not all in his ears. He reined in, and turned his horse. Another horse trotted aimlessly at the far end of the lists—and its saddle was empty! Roger's vision cleared. There, in the center of the lists, flat on his back with his arms outflung, lay Sir Fulke le Manz, the great Sir Fulke, unhorsed, defeated, knocked out by an untried knight!

Pol came running, yelling incoherently. The world became a sea of faces, Sir Bertran's, Percivale Bonfilz', a multitude of others he didn't know. They talked endlessly, but Roger didn't hear what they said. He knew, as if in a dream, that he was being led back to his pavilion, was being helped out of his harness, was lying down on the rough pallet which was the tent's only furnishing. Then he slept.

★   ★   ★

Fulke left that night. No one saw him go.

Roger did not ride in the next day's jousting. He took part in the melee, and was surprised to find how easy it was to send a knight over his horse's crupper; but the high point of the tournament had come and gone in that one meeting with Fulke le Manz.

As he rode away from Odesham on the day after the feast that ended the tourney, Roger felt a little conceit. Why not? He had come there an untried, unknown knight; he was leaving with a reputation: the man who had beaten Sir Fulke le Manz and had won the crown of the tournament.

182

He smiled, recalling the moment when he had ridden around the lists with the flower chaplet on the point of his lance—the chaplet it was his privilege, as undisputed champion, to award to the Queen of Love and Beauty.

The girls had all fluttered like so many sparrows. Yvonne? Of course not. He had given the chaplet to sweet little Agatha, the only one who had been kind to him when he was an unproven boy. It was the least he could do for her. He might even go to see her again, sometime.

Agatha had her own ideas about that. While Roger was full of his triumph, wasting hardly a thought on the girl he had chosen Queen of Love and Beauty, Agatha was planning her wedding gown. Girls were the same eight hundred years ago as they are now. Just a year after the tournament at Castle Odesham, Agatha Fitzwarin and Roger de Wyke were married. Agatha, too, won a notable triumph at the great Odesham tournament.

Almost exactly a hundred years after young Sir Roger won the tournament at Odesham, his great-great-grandson took part in another, before the great King Edward I, known as "Longshanks."

He looked about the same as Roger had. He was covered in chain mail and wore a surcoat with the de Wyke arms on it. There were a few minor differences: he wore elbow and knee guards of the tough "courboilly," or boiled leather; he belted his sword differently; pieces of plate armor helped protect his shins and forearms. Best of all, his heavy tilting-helm did not sit directly on his head; its weight came on his shoulders.

The tournament had not changed much either, but the change was significant. It was a little less like war and a little more like a game. Rules were more strict, and fewer competitors got killed or badly hurt.

This de Wyke—his name was Hubert—fought with King Edward Longshanks in Wales and Scotland, and was killed at the battle of Bannockburn in 1314. In that battle, the best of the English chivalry was soundly beaten by the Scots, not by Scottish knights but by ranks of stubborn soldiers holding long pikes. There was a note of warning in this for the knights, but they paid little attention. They were still riding high.

The science of making armor had progressed. Armorers were putting pieces of plate on top of the mail—just tying them there with thongs. This worked pretty well, and certainly gave added protection. Gradually, almost the whole body became covered by bits and pieces of plate, fastened to the mail underneath by straps or rivets. They had not yet figured out any way of protecting such vital parts of the body as the armpits or the base of the throat, and mail showed there. The whole effect was clumsy and patchy, and the men who had to wear the armor covered it up as best they could with a gay outer garment of cloth. In Chaucer's time, a knight could be fully armored and yet have hardly any metal showing.

This period, the three hundred years between chain mail and the time when armor was all plate, was called the "transition period," and it was a wonder that knights of that period could move at all. Compared to them, Roger in his mail hauberk was as free as a basketball player.

Over a knight's underclothing came the gambeson; then the suit of mail; then another gambeson, perhaps padded like the first one; then the plate, with its various pieces fastened together or tied to the gambeson; then the surcoat, called a "pourpoint," brilliant with colors—and it was often padded too! A chubby knight, packed into an outfit like that, must have been nearly as wide as he was tall.

The old, clumsy helm was discarded early, except for tournaments. It was just too much to wear on a military campaign. In its place came a head-covering known as a basinet, which looked something like the old cone-shaped helmet Drogo had worn centuries earlier. It was constructed better, though, and came down to protect the ears and the nape of the neck. The old mail coif was gone, too; in its place was a piece of mail, called a camail, which hung down like a curtain attached to the bottom of the basinet.

The helmet did not protect the face at first, but armorers began experimenting with movable visors which could be raised—or sometimes opened like the door of a stove—when the knight was not actually fighting. Then came movable chinpieces.

The last part of the body to be protected by plate was, as you might expect, the armpit. This is a very vulnerable spot, especially when the arm is raised to wield a sword. There really is no very good way to cover the armpit with plate armor, unless you're prepared to go around with your arms sticking out at right angles to your body. Armorers finally designed a round piece called a "gouchet," which hung down in front and must have been miserably uncomfortable. But at least it warded off everything but a blow from underneath.

It would be tedious to go through all the stages of the slow evolution of armor from the time of Richard the Lion-Hearted to King Henry VIII, four hundred years later. Fashions came and went, and fashions were as important in armor as in everyday clothes. At one stage long, pointed toes were attached to the iron shoes, so long that it was impossible to walk in them and they had to be added after the knight had mounted. They served no earthly purpose, but it was the fashion and a knight had to be in style, at all costs. At another period the armored shoes were broad and stubby, like bear paws. There were suits of armor made in imitation of ordinary dress, even to flounces and puffs and bowknots made of steel. There was armor of courboilly, of brass, even armor made to imitate that of the ancient Romans.

The basinet gave way to a helmet called a salade, or sallet, popular in Germany. It looked something like a fireman's helmet, except that it came down over the upper part of the face and was worn with a fixed chinpiece. That, in turn, gave way to a completely closed helmet called an armet, which provided almost perfect protection but must have been stiflingly hot.

In the fifteenth century—Columbus' century—the armorers really went to work. They had figured out ways to protect the whole body, and now they turned to making the armor lighter, stronger, and more comfortable. A knight's whole body was covered by plate, and the under coating of mail was done away with, except for scraps to cover the armpits and elbows. Breastplates were of two pieces, which could slide one over the other and give greater freedom of movement. The armorers also invented various kinds of sliding rivets and hooks. The whole trend, in fact, was toward making armor of more and smaller pieces, beautifully fitted and fastened together.

By this time, a fine suit of armor was a real work of art, and the man who owned such a costly outfit wanted to show it off. All the velvet surcoats and pourpoints vanished, and the armored knight stood forth—a splendid figure in gleaming steel, impressive, dignified, awesome.

Unfortunately, by then the knight was out of date. He didn't know it yet, but he was. A number of things brought about his downfall, but they boiled down to the fact that the world had passed him by. A knight in shining armor was just an expensive luxury, hardly worth having around in a battle.

For one thing, there was the longbow. Bows had been used for a long time, of course. Oriental archers were shooting their arrows before the dawn of history. But in Western Europe, bows were comparatively feeble weapons, almost useless against a mail-clad rider.

Then the English, trying to subdue the troublesome Welshmen in their mountains, ran up against a different sort of weapon altogether. This was the longbow—a bow six feet long or more, which discharged an arrow with force enough to fly a hundred yards, split a knight's chain mail, go through his thigh, the mail on the other side of his leg, a leather and wooden saddle, and finally embed itself in the unfortunate horse. From the viewpoint of the knights, it was a cowardly trick to stand off and shoot arrows instead of standing still and getting spitted on a lance. But it was a trick that worked. The English adopted the longbow, improved on it, and made it their national weapon.

This was considerably later than the time of Sir Roger and King Richard the Lion-Hearted, in spite of Ivanhoe and the romances written about Robin Hood and his merry men in Sherwood Forest. Richard died in 1199, killed by a bolt from a crossbow, and never lived to see the day when English archers were masters of a battlefield.

Richard had no business to be where he was when he got killed. He was trying to capture a castle and get his hands on some treasure he thought was there. Nevertheless, his death occasioned new outbursts of anger on the part of the knights against that "cowardly"

weapon, the crossbow. (On his deathbed, King Richard ordered that the soldier who had shot him be pardoned. He wasn't. They skinned him alive. They weren't too far from barbarians, even then.)

Crossbows were devilish contrivances which could pierce mail with no trouble. Resentment against the crossbow, or arbalest, was so strong that a Pope prohibited its use against Christians, although it was perfectly all right to kill heathens with it.

The knights weren't beaten yet, though. They had an answer to both longbow and arbalest: more armor. They lost mobility and speed, but by encasing themselves in well-tempered plate they stayed nearly invulnerable. They paid for it.

The knight's main value in warfare had been the terrific headlong charge, the irresistible onslaught that nothing could stand against. But arrows and crossbow bolts could kill horses, too, and so they had to begin covering their steeds with armor, losing still more speed. Finally, the knight's smashing charge degenerated into a slow, clumsy trot. But then something newer came along, something even more bewildering and efficient and terrible: Guns.

The first firearms appeared on the battlefield about the time of Chaucer. They didn't amount to much at first; in fact, they weren't nearly so effective as a longbow. And they were about as likely to blow up the gunner as whatever he was aiming at. They were slow, too, and clumsy—not as accurate as a brickbat and without much more range.

But they had advantages.

An arbalest strong enough to pierce mail could not be wound up without a device like a windlass, and this was miserably slow. Longbows were handier and ten times as fast, but they were temperamental weapons, affected by damp and wind. More than that, it took years of practice to make an expert archer, or even an arbalestier.

Guns were different.

They were cheap. And they were easy to work. Any bacon-brain could be taken from a plow and taught in a few minutes to touch a slow-match to an iron tube. That's all it took to slaughter the noblest knight who ever rode on horseback.

The complaints of the noble knights against crossbows were as nothing to their howls of rage over "crakys of warre." They considered gunners not quite human, in league with the devil. The gallant Chevalier Bayard, the knight without fear and without reproach, made a practice of hanging every gunner he could get his hands on, and most other knights applauded him.

It did no good. More gunners came along. And more.

It wasn't only such things as longbows and guns that doomed the knight in armor. The world was changing, too. The old, wild, lawless days were going, and a modern world was emerging. In this new world, there was no place for him. It was a world of politics, of commerce, of buying and selling and making money. Roger would not have understood it; still less would Drogo the Red. Trying to explain it to Huberic Split-Chin would have been like trying to explain it to an Iroquois war chief. (It would have made sense to old Quintus Rufinus Strabo, though.)

The knight who made songs to his ladylove and fared forth to do great deeds in her honor, with her sleeve tied to his helm, was admired and respected in the twelfth century. In the sixteenth century he was laughed at, like Don Quixote.

It wasn't that the world was getting more peaceful. Far from it. In early modern times wars may not have been as incessant as they had been in the days of Count Rolf and Charlemagne, but they were bigger and bloodier and probably more cruel. The old system of mounted knights and squires, plus a few professional soldiers and an untrained army of serfs, was no longer the answer. In early medieval times, warfare was anything but scientific. Three-quarters of an army was likely to consist of unhappy farmers who had been drafted by their feudal overlords and had no interest whatever in the matter themselves. They wanted only to get back to their fields.

It became obvious that it was far smarter to leave the serfs on their farms and fight wars with professional soldiers. Money was getting plentiful enough so that mercenaries could be paid. Besides, the old class of lesser nobility, from which most of the fighting knights had come, was getting less and less interested in warfare as a means of livelihood. They were becoming landowners and courtiers instead of fighting men.

Kings of the countries which were forming out of the old feudal patchwork did not want jealous, quarrelsome, ambitious chieftains struggling among themselves for power. Rather than have a baron who would bring five hundred of his own men into the army, a king preferred to have five hundred men of *his* own, paid from the royal treasury.

There were as many reasons for the decline of the feudal system as there were for the decline of the ancient Roman Empire: greater wealth, greater security, the rise of the merchant class, the centralization of power, the growth of a legal system, even the Black Death and other plagues which made labor scarce and wages high.

All these factors, and more, helped bring about the dethroning of the armored knight as the hero of the battlefield. And besides long bows and guns, still another menace was arising: the disciplined foot soldier.

As long as infantry was nothing but a formless mob, mostly scared serfs with pruning-hooks or knives, the knight on his horse had nothing whatever to fear from them. About all they did was get in his way; a single knight in full armor, mounted on an armored horse, could cut a path through a thousand of them.

But some countries—Switzerland, for example, and Scotland—were too small or too poor to support these gorgeous but costly human tanks. Switzerland was rich in only one thing: she had plenty of tough mountaineers, muscled like bulls from climbing Alps, who shared a fierce desire for freedom. They didn't like to be ordered around.

The small countries discovered that well-drilled and courageous men on foot, properly armed, could not only stand up to a charge of armored knights, but make them wish they'd never come charging.

They rediscovered the old phalanx of Alexander the Great, or a modification of it. They developed a variety of long-handled weapons and learned how to use them. And they began to succeed. An early example was the battle of Bannockburn, already noted, where Scottish "schiltrons"—massed pikemen—taught the English knights a hard lesson.

It took a great deal of calm courage, discipline, and endless drill to stand unflinchingly before a charge of armored knights. Often the pike-mass did not work, and the foot soldiers were ridden into the ground. But often it did work, and horsemen riding against them were spitted like a frankfurter on a fork. If the spears did not impale the knights, at least they slowed them down, and other spearmen finished off the job.

Foot soldiers had a great variety of these long-handled weapons. All were developed from farm tools like pruning hooks and hayforks. The halberd, the Swiss national weapon, is familiar. It looks like a combination of spear, ax, and pick, and in the hands of a brawny Switzer it was sudden death. The Swiss Guards at the Vatican still carry them. There were other kinds of weapons for fighting on foot: poleaxes, glaives, gisarmes, partizans, ox-tongues, warforks. Some had a spring device which could clamp around the arm or neck of a knight and haul him off his horse like a sack of flour. Some tried to do too many things at once and had so many blades and points it's hard to see how they worked at all.

It took a long time before the armored knight finally admitted he was through. Cities in America were already old when battles in Europe were still seeing the charge of men in armor, in spite of cannon, hand-guns, drilled infantry, and other new ideas.

Long after knights had all but abandoned armor for the battle-field, they wore it in their mock battles. Tournaments were still popular, more popular than ever, but they had become less and less dangerous. Sir Roger de Wyke would have sneered at the tournaments which his descendant, Thomas Wyke, fought under the eyes of Queen Elizabeth I. (Thomas didn't enjoy them much, but every-body of his rank and age was expected to take part. He preferred to write poetry and go to the theater. He wrote a poem, once, to the stone knight on the tomb; he had played on the old tomb as a boy. Thomas knew, vaguely, that the stone knight was an ancestor of his, but nobody could tell him much more.

This Elizabethan Wyke (the family had dropped the "de" by then) also wrote a poem to another ancestor of his, one Sir Richard, who lay buried under a brass slab near the tomb of the Crusader. Sir Richard had fought in France in the Hundred Years' War, under the great King Edward III and his son the Black Prince, about two hundred years before Thomas wrote his poem. When Sir Richard fought, in basinet and pourpoint, the great days of knighthood were all but over, and Richard, who was an intelligent man, realized it. The fact was brought home to him forcefully, one autumn day outside a little French city.

For some time the country had been full of the signs of war: burned houses, stripped fields, discarded weapons, an occasional dead body. Now, ahead of him, Harry the Gunner saw the high walls of the town of Corbec, its banners still defiantly flying. A hard nut to crack, this little French city. An English army encircled it, but no Englishman had yet set his foot inside its thick stone walls.

The ox-drawn gun cart was maddeningly slow. If it made a half-mile in an hour, it was doing well. The wooden wheels groaned and grated under the tremendous weight of the big cannon, and the driver kept up a constant stream of talk to his four patient beasts.

English soldiers were beginning to appear, foragers mostly, scouring the stripped countryside for food. Harry, his assistant, and even the driver paid them no heed. These foragers were not true soldiers, just part of the rabble that went with every army. But the four men coming toward them from the direction of the English camp were a different matter. They walked with the erect, arrogant stride of the real fighting man. Their faces were brown and hard. Their leather coats and iron basinets, although worn, were well cared for. Two of the four had longbows slung on their backs and a quiver of arrows at their belts. All of them wore short swords.

197

One of the four, a big man with a bristling brown beard, stopped short as he saw the cart with its huge bombard. "Ha!" he shouted, and spat into the dust of the road. "Here it comes! One of the devil's weapons, lads. One o' them thunderers!"

"We want none o' them around here," one of his companions snarled. "This is a good war, this is. Here comes noise and stink."

"Aye, but it'll take more than noise and stink to root the Frenchies out from behind their walls," Brown-Beard remarked sourly. "Guns! How I hate 'em! Spoiling the trade of good archers, is all they're good for."

Harry paid no attention. He was used to the fact that most archers, and all knights and men-at-arms, bitterly hated the thing he loved most: his big iron bombard which could throw an 80- to 200-pound stone ball at a target a half-mile away. Like most bombards, it was made of heavy iron bars welded together in a cylinder, reinforced by thick bands of iron. The gun was seven feet long, mounted on a wooden framework which allowed it to be raised and lowered, although clumsily. Harry called the great weapon "Lioness" because it roared so loudly, and he never referred to Lioness as "it"—always "she."

Lioness had never been tried out in battle. For that matter, neither had Harry, but the thought of battle didn't worry him. He thought of himself, insofar as he thought about the matter at all, not as a soldier but as a craftsman. Battle, to him, did not mean war cries, flashing swords, and thundering hooves. It meant a problem: how quickly could Lioness punch her way through a stone wall? He was anxious to find out.

Harry had a lot of confidence in Lioness. She had done very well in practice, and had killed only one man, an incautious apprentice who peered down the muzzle to see why the charge had not gone off. Through the rough Channel crossing and the slow trip over the once-fair land of France, Harry had tended Lioness as a mother tends her baby. And the bombard was his baby.

Harry had begun life like his father, as a blacksmith. But the soldiers, passing the smithy on their way to the wars in France, had so dazzled him by their talk of the new weapon that when he finally saw one, he fell in love with it. That had been ten years ago. Now he was a master gunner, mixer of his own powder, loader, pointer, and firer. He had helped make Lioness. Harry was thirty years old, without wife or family or attachments—except the huge gun.

The English camp was closer now. On the walls of the French town, Harry could see an occasional bright flash, the armor of a defender. He grinned. By now they must have seen that the English were bringing up a bombard. How they must be quaking!

More soldiers began running toward them from the camp. Guns had been part of an army for some time, but they were still new and rare enough to be a novelty. The four archers stayed with Harry and Lioness, talking more loudly and cursing more bitterly all the time.

"Clear the way, there!" the ox-driver shouted.

Harry jumped up on the wagon. "Make way ahead!" he yelled. "We've come to punch a hole in the walls for you!"

There were a few cheers, but most of the soldiers scowled and muttered and many hissed. Harry felt a thump on the wagon, and turned to see that Brown-Beard, the archer, had jumped up beside him.

"See this?" the archer bawled, stamping on the black barrel of Lioness. "See this ugly monster? Punch a hole in the walls! Lads, I've seen these things at work, and they couldn't punch a hole in a dairymaid's undershirt! All they're good for is to make noise and smoke, and blow up honest soldiers like us!"

The crowd, by now several hundred, responded with a cheer, and Harry noticed that the ones who were the least honest and soldierly-looking cheered the loudest. He was beginning to get a trifle apprehensive. So closely was the mob packed that the cart could not move, and more men were running up all the time.

"Turn it over!" someone shouted. "Don't let the devil's machine into the camp!"

There was a roar of approval. Brown-Beard jumped up on top of Lioness. "There speaks a brave man! Come on! Tip it over! Throw this monster into the road!"

Furious, Harry vaulted up beside the archer. "You're crazy, archer. All of you are crazy! We're sent here by the King himself, Edward of Windsor! We're going to crack the shell of this town!"

He caught Brown-Beard by the arm. "Keep away from my gun!" he ordered.

The archer swung his free arm, clouting Harry on the ear. He was taller than the gunner by a head, but after all, Harry was a blacksmith and his arms were thick and powerful. He slammed his fist into the archer's bushy chin and knocked him, kicking, into the close-pressed crowd below. It only made them more furious. With angry yells, they began trying to swarm aboard the cart.

"Stop! Back!" In all the uproar, no one had heard the approach of a group of riders, armored knights and men-at-arms, led by the commander of the siege army himself, the Earl of Wintringham. "Back, you rioting pack of mongrels!" the earl shouted, and his followers echoed him, laying about with the flat of their swords.

Sullenly, the mob melted away. "Take care, Earl!" a hoarse voice called. "He'll blow you up higher'n a cathedral spire, he will!" There were hoots of laughter, which the earl ignored.

"You took long enough to get here," the earl said sourly. "I expected you a week ago." His expression was no more friendly than the soldiers' had been. He hated the gun as much as they did, probably more, but he knew he needed the enormous power of this big metal tube if he were ever to get inside Corbec.

"We came as quick as we could, my lord," Harry began. "We can't travel more—"

The earl signaled for silence. "I want no talk from you—only from the bombard. How soon can you have it set up and ready?"

"Two hours, my lord."

"See that you do. We must end this siege soon." He turned to an elderly knight beside him, a knight who bore on his pourpoint the blazon of a golden lamp. "Sir Richard, I pray you stay by this—this devil's instrument, and keep the rabble away. Take what men-at-arms you need."

"Yes, my lord," Sir Richard de Wyke answered.

202

The earl bent another disapproving glance at Lioness. "I hate to ask any of my knights to have anything to do with guns," he said. "I shall be back to see this prodigy perform."

Sir Richard smiled slightly. "I have done stranger things as a soldier, my lord."

The earl and most of his retinue rode off. The cart got under way again, creaking and groaning, with Sir Richard and a dozen armed men riding alongside. The knight had little to say. He examined Lioness keenly with frosty gray eyes, and a dangling hook on the visor of his basinet clinked faintly as he shook his head. But Harry had other things to worry about.

Most important was the proper placing of his bombard. By rights, he should have taken time to study carefully the entire wall of the town to hunt for weak places where the big stone balls would have the most destructive effect. But the earl was in a hurry. He would have to depend on the advice of the knight. Harry asked Sir Richard to show him the weakest spot in the wall.

"I thought your gun could smash any stonework," Sir Richard said.

"So she can, sir," Harry replied loyally. "No wall can stand in front of Lioness. But she'll break through quicker where the wall is weakest."

The knight nodded. "That stands to reason. Lioness, eh? Because it—I beg your pardon, because *she* has a loud roar?"

"Partly, sir. But mostly because nothing can stand against her."

"I hope you've named her well." Sir Richard explained that the English had reason to believe the French defenders had been at work strengthening their wall from the inside. The big English trebuchets, which flung stones high into the air, hadn't made much impression on the defenses. But just outside a round tower to the left of the gate —the knight pointed in that direction—he thought there was a place which would yield to battering. "The trebuchets haven't done more than start a little crack there," he said. "They mend it as fast as we make it. But there's your weak spot."

Harry nodded. When he looked at the place in the wall, he could see a streak of lighter color, fresh mortar filling the crack made by the trebuchet stones.

He directed the driver of the cart toward a place about three hundred yards in front of the weak spot. Sir Richard watched with interest as Harry supervised the enormous task of getting Lioness ready to go to work. It took an immense amount of bone-breaking effort by fifty men to lower her down a ramp from the wagon and set her up on her wooden frame, her big muzzle pointing toward the crack in the wall.

Soldiers crowded round again. Even Brown-Beard came close. He scowled and spat, but said nothing. Some knights came drifting up, brave in their armor and gay pourpoints, under tall nodding plumes or crests. Most of the onlookers were quiet, but a few of the knights made remarks. "I wish those things never had been made," one said in a clear, penetrating voice. "If I were running this army, no gun or gunner would come within ten miles of it."

If you were running this army, Harry thought, everybody might as well pack up and go home. It was obvious, though, that the other knights agreed with their comrade. "They are an affront to knighthood, a shame to England, and a blot on Christianity," one said.

"Besides," a third knight added in an affected lisp, "they stink so abominably!"

After much tugging and hauling, Lioness was finally set to Harry's satisfaction. If he had gauged his distance right, the shot should smash directly into the crack in the wall. Then again, it might not. No one knew that better than Harry the Gunner. So many things could go wrong! The powder he would mix might be in the wrong proportion. He might pack it too tightly, and then it would not ignite and he would have the immensely dangerous job of taking it out again. Or he might pack it too loosely, in which case it would only go "whoosh."

The gun might go off too soon, or not go off at all, or the whole thing might explode and kill everyone within thirty yards' radius. Such things happened with guns.

While his assistant picked up the roundest of the shaped stone shot and lined them up near Lioness, Harry bent to the dangerous job of mixing the powder. This had to be done just before firing; otherwise the charcoal separated from the other components and nothing happened.

Before he began, he turned to Sir Richard. "Sir Knight, I pray you, would you cause the gentlemen and soldiers to stand further off?"

The knight raised his eyebrows, probably at the thought of taking orders from such a lowly creature as a blacksmith turned gunner, but he passed the instructions on to his squire courteously enough. "Back!" the squire shouted. "Back, and give the devil's apprentice room!"

"Silence, sirrah!" Sir Richard roared. "The man is an Englishman, whatever you think of his trade!"

Abashed, the squire deleted the "devil's apprentice" from his shout, and contented himself with warning everybody of the imminent danger of being blown to bits. The mob of soldiers moved back speedily. The knights followed, but slowly and with dignity, as if they did not want anyone to see they were afraid of the strange rites Harry was performing. Only Sir Richard stood close by, watching with absorption as Harry measured out the charcoal and saltpeter into a wooden tub, and gingerly began to mix in sulfur with a wooden paddle.

"Sir," he warned again, "this is a chancy business. I pray you, retire to a safer place."

The knight shook his head. "What you dare, gunner, I dare. And I think a man of war should know something about this strange new art of yours. I saw what the cannons did at Crécy."

Harry knew all about Crécy. The cannons hadn't done much—puny little things, not like his majestic Lioness. It had been the English longbows that won the day at Crécy, fourteen years earlier. Carefully, he mixed his powder, watching the color, feeling the texture, even tasting it. Finally he nodded, satisfied.

"I am ready, Sir Richard," he said.

The knight raised his hand in a signal. Harry looked up to see the earl himself, with his followers, sitting on horses a hundred yards away. The earl in turn raised his hand.

"Proceed, gunner," Sir Richard said.

There was a hush over the whole army as Harry, slowly and with extreme care, took a ladle of powder from the tub—a wooden ladle; iron must never come close, for fear of sparks—and carried it toward the bombard. Still slowly and even more carefully, he put it down Lioness' yawning mouth and tamped it down, calculating by the feel when it had reached just the right consistency. He added another ladle of powder, and after a measuring glance at the distance to the wall, part of a third.

More powder, poured into the touchhole, and he was ready. Then his assistant came up, holding a twist of flaming tow. Harry took one last sight. The parapet of the town walls was crowded with defenders—but the point at which the bombard was aimed was vacant. The Englishmen, except Sir Richard, clapped their hands over their ears. Harry laid the fire to the priming powder at the touchhole.

And nothing happened.

The priming powder flared up with a tiny puff. No roar, no stone ball hurtling toward the walls. There was a tiny far-away cheer from the French, and then a loud and raucous hooting from the English. Over the laughter and uproar, the voice of the lisping knight could be heard: "Devil's apprentice, is he? He'll never be promoted to journeyman!"

"Melt it down for arrowheads!" bawled Brown-Beard.

Someone else shouted, "We waited three weeks for *that?*"

The sudden release of tension had all the Englishmen guffawing, shouting "Boom!" and dancing around like trained bears—in general, having a huge joke at Harry's expense. Harry was annoyed, but that was all. Guns were tricky and temperamental, another reason why they were generally called "she." The best gunner never knew exactly what was going to happen when flame met powder. "By your leave, sir," he said to Sir Richard. "I'll try again." The knight nodded. There was a twinkle in his gray eyes.

A thunder of hoofs, and the earl drew up beside them. "What play-acting is this?" he demanded angrily. "Are you playing games, gunner?"

"He will try again, my lord," said Sir Richard.

The earl grunted, and stayed where he was. "Best move back, my lord," Harry warned. "Your horse—"

"My horse will not be frightened by a finger-snap," the earl said. "Go on with your cannon-shooting."

Obediently, Harry swabbed out the touchhole with a damp cloth, put in another charge of priming with meticulous care, and called again for the blazing tow. The assistant brought it. Harry laid it to the powder.

This time the gun went off.

The noise split the heavens. Accustomed to it as he was, Harry had to fight for breath for a second when the wave of concussion hit him. A thick, stinking cloud of dirty brown smoke hid everything from his view. Except that he could see the stone projectile, high in the air and traveling almost lazily, flying toward its target.

Harry turned. The earl lay flat on his back on the ground. His horse, mad with fright, was dashing off wildly. Half the crowd of

onlookers were scrambling to put more distance between them and this devilish contrivance. Even the knights galloped away. Only Sir Richard stood, looking a little dazed, powder smoke staining his pourpoint.

There was a smashing, crumbling noise. Harry's aim had been excellent. A wide, U-shaped hole yawned at the top of the wall, just above the crack.

"Shall I try again, Sir Richard?" Harry asked calmly.

"Yes," the knight said. "Try again." Harry had the odd notion that there was unhappiness in his eyes.

Two more rounds went sailing out from the bombard. Harry miscalculated one; it hit the ground and skipped over it to smash into fragments against the wall. But the other widened the U-shaped hole. Drums clattered and feet pounded on the earth as the English commanders summoned their men for an assault. At this rate, a big part of the wall would be down before dark.

As Harry measured powder for a fourth round, he heard shrill cries of excitement and alarm. He looked up. The town gates were open, and from them poured a stream of horsemen in armor, holding their lances ready.

"Ha!" breathed Sir Richard. "A sally. I've been expecting this. They mean to destroy the gun."

The French riders pounded toward Lioness, paying no attention to the arrows which began to fall among them, or the English riders who spurred swiftly forward. Straight for Lioness they rode. Harry could hear them shouting.

Destroy Lioness? As quickly as he dared, he packed down the powder in the bombard's gaping maw. "Stones!" he shouted. "The bag of stones!" His assistant came hurrying up with a coarse fiber bag filled with pebbles of various sizes. Harry pushed it down after the powder and raced to add priming.

The French riders were dangerously close. Sunlight glinted from their armor. The pennons on lance points fluttered bravely, and the painted shields were brilliant and gay. Harry felt the earth shake under the pounding of hoofs.

He grabbed the blazing tow and touched it to the vent. Again the ear-splitting roar, the great billow of greasy smoke, then silence.

Where the French riders had been there was nothing, nothing but some piles of torn flesh, some rags of cloth, some battered bits of metal. Only a dozen Frenchmen, dazed and shaken, were still mounted, and English riders were closing on them fast.

"They thought they'd wreck my Lioness," Harry said to Sir Richard. He grinned through the black mask the smoke had left on his face. "She answered them. They won't try that again."

The knight turned his gaze from the struggle before him. The last of the Frenchmen were being cut down by yelping English men-at-arms. "Oh, yes, gunner, they will try it again. Brave knights will ride out against those cannons of yours, again and again."

"Doesn't worry me," Harry said. "They won't get as far as Lioness."

The knight smiled. Again Harry had the impression of sadness. "Sometimes they will. But there will always be more cannon and more gunners." He drew his sword and looked along its flashing length. "There is still some work for this to do. But not for long, I think, not for long. What is a sword, or a lance, or armor, or even a longbow and arrows, against that Lioness of yours and her cubs?"

"Not much good, and that's a fact," Harry said.

Sir Richard sheathed his sword. "I'm glad I'm getting old, gunner. I had my youth when there were no guns. I laughed at lances then, but I can't laugh at your Lioness." He turned, and made a gesture of farewell. "Good-by, gunner. Batter the wall down with your powder and shot."

Harry watched the knight for a minute. The gold lamp on the shoulder of his pourpoint gleamed. Not a bad sort of man for a knight, Harry thought. Talked funny, though. Laugh at lances! He shrugged, and went back to his powder tub.

But when Sir Roger de Wyke rode through the Holy Land on that hot day in the year 1191, no thought of guns, or of the decline of armored knights, came to trouble him. Roger shepherded his little army back to King Richard. He was at the side of the Lion Heart when the Crusaders stood within sight of the Holy City of Jerusalem. A year later, with more scars on his body, Sir Roger went back to England and to the Lady Agatha.

He lived to see his sons grown men, and to help his grandsons learn the trade which had been his and which would be theirs: the trade of fighting as an armored knight. When, at last, Sir Roger went to join his forefathers in the little church, the Lady Agatha had a famed stonemason carve his tombstone.

The mason wanted to show Sir Roger lying peacefully, his hands clasped in prayer, as the custom was. But Lady Agatha would have none of it. She insisted that the mason show Sir Roger rising, as if to answer a call to battle.

"For," she said, "he was no meek man. Brave he was, and I would have that shown on his stone. He was quarrelsome sometimes, as well, and reckless too." She added wistfully, "But he was always courteous and gentle to me, and to all under his protection. And never once in his life did he break faith with God or with any man."

A good epitaph, for a good knight. Let it stand as the epitaph for all the other good knights who lived, fought, and died, so many years ago.